# AND KANGAROOS

## (NEW WRITING SCOTLAND 17)

Edited by

**MOIRA BURGESS**
and
**DONNY O'ROURKE**

with Rody Gorman (Gaelic Adviser)

Association for Scottish Literary Studies

Association for Scottish Literary Studies
c/o Department of Scottish History, 9 University Gardens
University of Glasgow, Glasgow G12 8QH


First published 1999

**British Library Cataloguing in Publication Data**

A CIP record for this book is available
from the British Library


ISBN 0–948877–41–3


Published with assistance from

Typeset by Roger Booth Associates, Hassocks, West Sussex

Printed by Cromwell Press Ltd, Trowbridge, Wiltshire

# CONTENTS

# INTRODUCTION

The year of a new parliament has been a particularly exciting time to be editing a volume of new Scottish writing. Will future critics find the fall-out of this national event in Scottish literature, as some have found the long shadow of the failed 1979 referendum? It can take a little while for these things to work through into fiction and poetry, but enquirers could start here.

Change has been in the air too at New Writing Scotland, as one of the editors comes to the end of his three-year term, while the other has her first experience of this demanding and delightful job. The sheer volume of contributions piling in each year – or should that be tonnage? Certainly it's easier to weigh them than count them – has been commented on by earlier editors, and so has the amount of extremely good material. In this respect at least nothing has changed. We could easily have filled three volumes of this size without compromising on quality. The advice to most unsuccessful contributors, therefore, remains the same: don't be discouraged. Your work is publishable and you'll get lucky before long. Send your rejected contributions elsewhere, and submit to us again – new work, please – next year.

The pieces in Friends and Kangaroos, therefore, represent not just the cream, but truly the *crème de la crème*, of new Scottish writing. What, exactly, has earned them their place? It's hard to say. We chose some for their technical dexterity, and some for their passion, and some, of course, for both. Occasionally there's a cat which one of the editors found herself unable to leave out. Occasionally there's a vampire which neither editor could resist. We were especially pleased to find the various languages of Scotland being explored and used in innovative ways, and if there's a theme this year, it may be that.

It may be, of course, that there isn't a theme at all. As is the lot of editors, we may find ourselves arraigned for what we have done and what we have failed to do. We do, however, think that this is a vintage year, and we present with pride the seventeenth annual volume of New Writing Scotland. Writing from a new Scotland, perhaps?

Moira Burgess
Donny O'Rourke

# NEW WRITING SCOTLAND 18

Submissions are invited for the sixteenth annual volume of *New Writing Scotland,* to be published in 2000, from writers resident in Scotland or Scots by birth or upbringing. Poetry, drama, short fiction or other creative prose may be submitted but not full-length plays or novels, though self-contained extracts are acceptable. The work must be neither previously published nor accepted for publication and may be in any of the languages of Scotland.

Your submissions should be typed, double-spaced, on one side of the paper only and the sheets secured at the top-left corner. Each individual work should be clearly marked with your name and address.

Please be aware that we have limited space in each edition, and therefore shorter pieces are more suitable – although longer items of exceptional quality may still be included. A maximum length of 3,500 words is suggested. Please send no more than two short stories and no more than six poems.

Submissions should be accompanied by two stamped addressed envelopes, with sufficient postage (one for a receipt, the other for return of MSS) and sent by **31 January 2000** to:

Duncan Jones
Managing Editor, *New Writing Scotland*
ASLS
c/o Dept of Scottish History
9 University Gardens
University of Glasgow
Glasgow G12 8QH
Tel: 0141 330 5309

Leila Aboulela

# MAJED

'What are you doing?' Hamid couldn't see her properly because he didn't have his glasses on. She was blurred over the kitchen sink, holding the bottle in her hand. She was not supposed to be holding that bottle. How did she get hold of it? He had hidden it behind the videos late last night, behind *Enter The Dragon*. He had washed his glass carefully over the kitchen sink, gargled with ASDA Protect, then crept into bed beside her, careful, very careful not to wake her or the two youngest ones. Majed slept in the cot in the corner of the room, the newborn baby slept with them in the double bed so that Ruqiyyah could feed her during the night. During the night when Hamid had to go to the toilet he tried to be careful not to wake them up. Though sometimes he did, bumping into Majed's cot, stumbling on a toy. One night he had found himself, almost too late, not in the toilet but surrounded by the shoes that littered the entrance to the flat. He was startled into full consciousness by the baby crying.

'Ruqiyyah, what are you doing?' He should make a lunge at her, stop her before it was too late. It was precious stuff she was threatening to pour down the drain. But the whole household was in his way. A pile of washing waiting to go into the washing machine, the baby, sunk down and small, in her seat on the floor. She was creamy and delicate, wearing tiny gloves so that she would not scratch herself. The kitchen table was in his way. Majed sat on his high chair covered in porridge, singing, banging the table with his spoon, Sarah talked to him and chewed toast. Robin scooped Rice Krispies into his mouth while staring at the box; Snap, Crackle and Pop flying and things you could send for if your parents gave you the money.

Ruqiyyah put the bottle down. But only because there were plates and baby bottles in the sink. She started to wash them up, water splashing everywhere.

She looked at Hamid and shook her head.

Hamid groaned. He was relieved he couldn't see her eyes, her blue eyes filled with tears maybe. She had not always been Ruqiyyah, she once was someone else with an ordinary name, a name a girl behind the counter in the Bank of Scotland might have. When she became Muslim she changed her name then left her husband. Robin and Sarah were not Hamid's children. Ruqiyyah had told Hamid horror stories about her previous marriage. She had left little out. When she went on about her ex-husband, Hamid felt shattered. He had never met Gavin (who wanted nothing to do with Ruqiyyah, Robin and Sarah and had never so much as sent them a bean), but that man stalked Hamid's nightmares. Among Hamid's many fears, was the fear of Gavin storming the flat, shaking him until his glasses fell off, 'YOU FILTHY NIGGER, STAY AWAY FROM MY FAMILY.'

'Ruqiyyah wait, I'll get my glasses.' He looked at the children. He looked back at her, made a face. When the children finished their breakfast and headed towards Children's TV, they could talk. They couldn't talk in front of Robin. He was old enough to understand, pick up things. He was sensitive. Hamid ruffled Robin's hair, said something jolly about Snap, Crackle and Pop. Robin smiled and this encouraged Hamid to be more jocular. Whenever Hamid was stressed, he changed into a clown. The hahaha of laughter covered problems. Hahaha had wheels, it was a skateboard to slide and escape on.

'I'll get my glasses.' He stumbled away. He needed the glasses. The glasses would give him confidence. He would be able to talk, explain. She was so good, so strong, because she was a convert. But he, he had been a Muslim all his life and was, it had to be said, relaxed about the whole thing. Wrong, yes it was wrong. He wasn't going to argue about that. Not with Ruqiyyah. Instead he would say ... he would explain, that on the scale ... yes on the scale (he was a scientist after all and understood scales), on the scale of all the forbidden things, it was not really so wrong, so bad. There were worse, much worse, the heavies, the Big Ones; black magic, adultery, abusing your parents (something the dreadful Gavin had done – *pushed the old dear round her living room* – may he rot in Hell on account of this for all eternity and more). Hamid would explain ... Once he put his glasses on and the world cleared up he would explain. Human weakness etc. and Allah is all-forgiving. That's right. Then a sad, comic face. A gentle hahaha. But she could counter that argument about forgiveness though. He must be careful. She would say that one has to repent first before one could be forgiven. And she would be right. Of course. Absolutely. He had every intention to repent. *Every* intention. But not now, not this minute, not today. A few more days, when he got himself sorted out, when this bottle was finished, when he finished his Ph.D., when he got a proper job and did not need to work evenings in ASDA.

He found his glasses near the bed between the baby lotion and the zinc and castor oil. He put them on and felt better, more focused, more in control. Ruqiyyah hadn't yet dealt with this room. There were nappies on the floor, folded up and heavy. She had, though, stripped the sheets off Majed's cot. There were soft cartoon characters on the plastic mattress. Hamid rescued the prayer mat off the nappy-covered floor and dropped it on the unmade bed. He opened the window for the smells in the room to go out and fresh air to come in. Outside was another grey day, brown leaves all over the pavements. A gush of rainy air, a moment of contemplation. *Subhan Allah*, who would have ever thought that he, Hamid, born and bred on the banks of the Blue Nile, would end up here with a Scottish wife, who was a better Muslim than he was. Why had he married her? Because of the residence visa, to solve his problem with the Home Office once and for all. A friend had approached him once after Friday prayers (he did sometimes go to the mosque for Friday prayers, he was not *so* useless), and told him about Ruqiyyah, how she was a new convert with two little ones, how she needed a husband to take care of her. And you Hamid, need a visa ... Why not? Why not? Ha ha. Is she pretty? Ha ha. There had been a time in Hamid's life when the only white people he saw were on the cinema screen, now they would be under one roof. Why not? He brushed his teeth with enthusiasm, sprayed himself with Old Spice, armed himself with the jolly laugh and set out to meet the three of them. Robin's shy face, the gaze of a child once bitten twice shy. A woman of average height, with bright anxious blue eyes, her hair covered with a black scarf, very conservatively dressed, no make-up. He breathed a sigh of relief that she was not lean like European women tended to be. Instead she was soft like his own faraway mother, like a girl he had once longed for in the University of Khartoum, a girl who had been unattainable. And if on that first meeting, Ruqiyyah's charms were deliberately hidden, they were obvious in her one-year-old daughter. Sarah was all smiles and wavy yellow hair, stretching out her arms, wanting to be carried, wanting to be noticed. After the awkwardness of their first meeting, a lot of hahaha, tantrums from Robin, desperate jokes, Hamid stopped laughing. He entered that steady place under laughter. He fell in love with the three of them, their pale needy faces, the fires that were repressed in them. His need for a visa, her need for security, no longer seemed grasping or callous. They were swept along by the children, his own children coming along, tumbling out soon, easily. Two years ago Majed, three weeks ago the baby. At school when Ruqiyyah and Majed went to pick up Robin, no one believed that they were brothers. Ruqiyyah with her children; two Europeans, two Africans. The other mothers outside the school looked at her oddly, smiled too politely. But Ruqiyyah could handle the other mothers, she had been through much worse. She had once escaped Gavin to a women's refuge, lived with rats and Robin having a child's equivalent of a nervous breakdown.

He must make it to the kitchen before she poured the Johnny Walker down the sink. He was angry. His secret was out and now that it was out it could not go back in again. It wasn't fair. If she was suspicious why hadn't she turned a blind eye, why had she

searched for the proof? It wasn't fair. These were his private
moments, late at night, all by himself, the children asleep,
Ruqiyyah asleep. The whole soft sofa to himself, a glass of whisky
in his hand, the television purring sights that held his attention,
kung fu, football, sumo wrestling, Prince Naseem thrashing someone. Anything that blocked out the thesis, the humiliating hours
spent mopping up ASDA's floor, the demanding, roving kids.
Anything cheerful, not the news, definitely not the news. The last
thing he wanted at that time of night were his brothers and sisters
suffering in the West Bank. His own warm, private moments, the
little man on the bottle of Johnny Walker. That little man was
Johnny, an average sort of guy and because he was walking, striding along with his top hat, he was a Walker, Johnny Walker. Or
perhaps because he *was* Johnny Walker, he was represented as
walking, striding along happily. It was interesting, but at the end it
didn't matter and that was what Hamid wanted at that time of
night. Things that didn't matter. At times he took his glasses off,
let the television become a blur, and he would become a blur too,
a hazy, warm, loveable blur. Nothing sharp, nothing definite.
Blurring things made them tolerable, made it possible to get by.
The exact number of years he had been a Ph.D. student. Don't
count, man, don't count. Laughter blurred things too. Hahaha.
His thesis was not going to make it. He must, his supervisor said,
*stretch himself*. His thesis now, as it stood, was *not meaty enough*.
There was a lot of meat in ASDA, shelves. When he cleaned
underneath them, he shivered from the cold. Not meaty enough.
Johnny Walker was slight and not at all meaty and he was all
right, successful, striding along brimming with confidence. Why
shouldn't a man with an unfinished thesis and an ego-bashing job
at ASDA sit up late at night, once in a while, settle down in front
of the television and sink in. Sink into the warmth of the whisky
and the froth of the TV. Once in a while?

Majed lunged into the room. He squealed when he saw Hamid
sitting on the bed. 'Majed, say *salaam*, shake hands.' Hamid held
his hand out. Majed took his fist out of his mouth and placed it,
covered in saliva, in his father's hand. Then he pointed to his cot,
transformed because the sheet wasn't on it. It wasn't often that
Ruqiyyah changed the sheets. Majed walked over to his cot mum-
bling exclamations of surprise. He put his hands through the bars
and patted the cartoon characters on the plastic mattress.
'Mummy's washing your sheet. You'll be getting a nice clean
sheet,' Hamid said. It was rare that the two of them were alone
together. Hamid held him up and hugged him, put him on his lap.
He loved him so much. He loved his smell and roundness, his tight
little curls and wide forehead. Majed was a piece of him, a purer
piece of him. And that love was a secret because it was not the

same love he felt for Robin and Sarah. He feared for Majed, throat-catching fear, while with Sarah and Robin he was calm and sensible. He dreamt about Majed. Majed crushed under a bus and Hamid roaring from the pain, that came from deep inside, that surfaced into sobs, then Ruqiyyah's voice, her hand on his cheeks, what's wrong, what's the matter and the wave of shame with the silent coolness of waking up. I'm sorry, I'm sorry, it's nothing, go back to sleep. The more he loved Majed and the newborn baby, the kinder Hamid was to Robin and Sarah. He must not be unjust. Ruqiyyah must never feel that he favoured their children over Robin and Sarah. It was a rare, precious moment when he was alone with Majed, no one watching them. He threw him up in the air and Majed squealed and laughed. He stood Majed on the bed and let him run, jump, fly from the bed into his outstretched arms. Then he remembered Ruqiyyah in the kitchen. The memory dampened the fun. He sent Majed off to join Sarah and Robin in front of the television (already the blocked-nose voice of *Rugrats* filled the flat) and he walked back to the kitchen.

Ruqiyyah was clearing the things off the kitchen table, the baby was asleep in her chair on the floor. With his glasses on now, Hamid could clearly see the whisky bottle. Two-thirds empty, two-thirds ... His heart sank, that much ... or had she already poured some out? No. No she hadn't. He knew what she was going to do. She was going to clear the kitchen, wash everything and put it away, then ceremoniously tip the bottle into the empty sink.

She started cleaning up Majed's high chair. Her hair fell over her eyes. She wore an apron with Bugs Bunny on it. She was beautiful, not like women on TV, but with looks that would have been appreciated in another part of the world, in another century. Her lips were naturally red. He had thought, before they got married, that she was wearing lipstick. She wore *hijab* when she went out, she got up at dawn and prayed. This seriousness that he didn't have, baffled him. Something Scottish she brought with her when she stepped into Islam. The story of her conversion amazed him as much as her stories about Gavin shocked and sickened him. She had read books about Islam. Books Gavin had snatched and torn up. Not because they were about Islam, but because she was sitting on her fat arse reading instead of doing what he wanted her to do.

She wanted to learn Arabic. Hamid would doze in bed and next to him she would hold *Simple Words in Arabic*, over the head of the baby she was feeding. 'How do you say this?' she would ask from time to time, nudging him awake. When Hamid read the Qur'án out loud (he went through religious spells in Ramadan and whenever one of the children fell ill), she said, 'I wish I could read like you.'

He started to help her tidy up. He closed the flaps on the box of Rice Krispies, put it away in the cupboard. When she finished wiping the table and started on the floor, he lifted up the baby's seat and put it on the table. If she would talk to him, shout at him, it would be better. Instead he was getting this silent treatment. He began to feel impatient. What had made her search for the bottle? A smell … ?

Attack is the best form of defence. Laughter blurs things, smoothes them over. Hahaha. He began to talk, he put on his most endearing voice, tried a joke. Hahaha. She didn't answer him, didn't smile. She pushed her hair away from her face, poured powder into the drawer of the washing machine. She bent down and began to load the washing into the machine. It was linen, the sheets that had been on Majed's cot. Hamid said, 'But how did you know? Tell me.'

She sat on her heels, closed the door of the washing machine. She said, 'You pissed in Majed's cot. You thought you were in the toilet.' She twisted the dial that started the wash cycle. 'I pretended to be asleep. He didn't wake up.'

There was a place under laughter, under the hahaha.

Hamid saw her stand up, pick up the Johnny Walker and pour what was left of it down the drain. She poured it carefully so that not a single drop splashed on the sink where later the children's bowls and bottles would wait to be washed.

**Meg Bateman**

## PÒG

Ar ciad phòg na pòig-dhealachaidh
is m' inntinn ga luasgadh fad an fheasgair
le blàths do bhilean,
mo chridhe ga lìonadh uair eile
le iargain gun fheum, is eadarainn
an Cuan Sgìth is fichead bliadhna,
's mi srì ri m' ùidh a tharraing
gu sgioblachadh dhèidheagan,
a' srì ri m' ùidh ortsa
thionndadh gu ùidh màthar.

## KISS

Our first kiss a kiss of parting,
and all evening my mind rocked
by the warmth of your lips,
my heart again swollen
by a useless longing, the Minch
and twenty years between us,
as I strive to turn my mind
to tidying up the toys,
strive to turn my desire
into the regard of a mother.

## AIR TILLEADH DHACHAIGH

'S fheàrr dùsgadh tron oidhche le casan beaga air a' chluasaig
na cadal gun bhriseadh ann an taigh-òsda uasal,
teilibhisean am falach ann am preasa mahogany,
bòrd-sgrìobhaidh san uinneig fo chùirtearan cosgail;
b' fheàrr m' fhuil ùr air an searbhaidearan sneachdaidh
is trod nan caileagan ann an taigh-nighe ceathach,
na lainnir nan rùmannan a bheireadh a' chreids' ort
gur duine eile an àite eile aig àm eile thu ...
'S fheàrr mo chaithris a-nochd fo ghealaich air chuthach,
's mo bheatha dol seachad gun fhianais, gun fhaochadh,
ceum m' athar a' dìosgail far nach eil e air an staidhre,
na taibhsean gun tuigsinn ag aomadh thar na leapa;
's fheàrr na an sògh, am bas-bhualadh 's an labhairt,
mo shlacaireachd leis gach crois, gach imcheist is bacadh
is làmhan a' phàidse mum thimcheall nan crios-teasairginn,
gus an gluais an latha gu feum 's gu misneachd mi.

## HOME AGAIN

Better being woken through the night by little legs on the pillow,
than unbroken sleep in a plush hotel,
a television hiding in a mahogany chest,
a bureau in the window under expensive curtains;
better my bright blood on their snowy towels
and the scolding of the girls in a steamy laundry
than the gleam of those rooms that would have you believe
you were another person in another age ...
Better my sleeplessness under a raving moon,
with my life relentlessly passing by without witness,
my father's step where he is not on the stair,
the uncomprehending ghosts bending over the bed;
better than the luxury, applause, talk,
my buffeting by every obstacle, doubt, complexity,
with the child's arms, a safety belt, around me,
till day moves me to usefulness and courage.

Gavin Bowd

# THE WESTERN WORLD

All this frustration
in an atmosphere
of disinfection.

At the altar we lean
for pints of beer
and the stripper queen

With Buffalo Bill
and circus Indians
for our Western will.

We await the fringe
of your promised sex
wed to the syringe.

We've come long miles
to avert our eyes
from your thrusting smile

Guaranteed come profit or loss,
taking the toll,
carrying the cross.

**Tom Bryan**

## ASH
*from 'the native trees of Achendrean'*
*Gaelic: uinsinn (pronounced ooshin)*

Norse, Yggsdrasil, The World Tree,
linking heaven and earth,
roots as deep as the tree is tall.
Last to leaf, last to drop leaf.
Sap holy to the newborn.

Leaf for dye and fodder,
handles and spear shafts, oars,
ploughs and wheel rims.
Pliancy as strength, patient tree,
the colour of dawn, a dove's throat,
cold rain.

The proverb: 'grows well, but kills
the tree that's near.'
Patience *often* has that effect
(a different kind of spear).

## BLACKTHORN
*from 'the native trees of Achendrean' Gaelic: draoighean*

Blackthorn bearded the river's lip,
hedged black cattle on their leeward grazing.
This place was *named* for its thorns,
dark thorns and bitter fruit,
a harvest better than both:

walking stick, sheleilaigh,
black sloes for man and finch,
soft nest for hare and mouse.

Now old men mourn their thornless moor:

'Better the bramble than the blackthorn,
but better the blackthorn than the devil.'

In vain, wild finches seek sloes
in the wasted bracken,
where the devil hacks and burns.

**Ron Butlin**

## ONE MORE EVENING WITH FRIENDS AND KANGAROOS

Phil caught sight of the Grey-hair Twins in the mirror, double-smiled at them, and waved an open fan of pointing first fingers in their direction:
Bastards, and you're drunk the pair of you.
He splashed some water on his face, and then tried lining the wet bits up to the hand-drier which blasted full-force or else cut out completely, off/on off/on, if he slipped even two inches either side. So he gave up. Having checked the twins had merged themselves back into one he started out on the long-haul return to his seat.
Franco's Office Bar – a windowless room of broken-down tables, chairs and drunks, beer alcove in one corner, toilet alcove in the other – was at its best late on. Evenings never started in Franco's but often ended up in the blur of its straightforward aim: to get drunks drunker. It was the place where no one felt out of place, ever. For the last three hours he, Mike and Steve had been sitting round a table steadied by the torn beer mats they'd jammed under one of the legs.
Mike was explaining something: What you're saying about last-minute flights is all very well, Steve, but the problem with self-catering –
Phil's elbow slid off the edge of the table – always a bad sign.
Haud steady, eh! For Christ's sake! Steve lifted his pint clear.
Mike started on about named accommodation; Steve brought in ATOL and charter regulations.
Then Steve wasn't there any more.
Phil had been to Skye, once. He chose a clear stretch of the table, carefully lowered and positioned his elbow dead-centre for balance, and let the rest of him follow: I was in Skye once. I was ten, maybe. The mist –
Mike had just mentioned Las Palmas, but his own momentum in leaning forwards kept the words coming: The mist, I'm saying, first thing in the morning – not to mention all fucking day – when it cleared, I'm saying –
Bumped into a friend of yours back there.
Several Steves, like a hand of face cards, were being shuffled just above him; out of the deal came a three-pint card trick that hovered over the table till he'd worked out which pint was the real one, and grabbed it. Managing to speak at the same time:
Who?
Mike was saying: You needed to get up early if you wanted to use the swimming pool. See, the way they do it in Majorca is –

Who? Who?

Turned intae a fucking owl now, have you, Phil?

I'm asking – who? That you bumped intae?

That friend of yours. The waste of space you lumbered us with before. The paper-bag champion, the boxer.

Sonny?

That's the clown. Didn't speak to him. Didn't even let on I'd seen him, not after last time.

Last time?

Him and his hard-man act – nearly got us barred, remember?

The shelves behind the bar were moving in time to the noise, and so were the walls: everywhere he looked was like scraps of somewhere else, and being blown round and round where he sat. If he stood up he'd maybe not stay up. If he could get himself stood up – Grabbing good hold of the table-edge – A few seconds to get himself balanced – Lifting up his eyes –

Whereabout? He'd get him a pint and explain he's with friends. No problem. The only way.

Mike was drawing a diagram and explaining something about airbeds.

Whereabout? Standing upright, nearly. The entire bar had surged up to meet him; then ebbed away layer at a time.

He kept saying the words he wanted till he got them out loud: Whereabout's Sonny? Whereabout's Sonny?

Near the phone, I said. Some state you're in. You all right?

Your round next, mind. And don't bring that clown back with you.

Tables, chairs, people, more tables, one of the chairs came away in his hands. With friends, he'd say. No problem. The toilet was empty this time. Near the phone. Swaying but keeping it clear of the shoes. Not so pissed. Not so pissed as to get himself pissed on. Near the phone. Hands washed. Drying them now, or trying to – still no paper towels. Fucking hand-drier, fucking wind-tunnel, more like. What the –? Kangaroo-flavoured condoms? A joke, no? No – fucking kangaroo flavoured right enough. Keep one jump ahead, eh!

Near the phone, Steve said.

Looking left, looking right and looking straight ahead like a good boy. No Sonny. Thank fuck.

No Sonny – no problem.

No problem but getting Franco up this end. Taking a good grip of the bar with his left hand, a good right foot to keep the rail steady – secure enough now to wave his tenner back and forwards:

Three pints heavy.

Phil, a chance you can make that four –?

Out of nowhere the Wreck of the Year was standing beside

him. Bruises instead of eyes, the rest of him scabs and cuts – and not from this year's shave either. Coat turned up at the sleeves.

OK, Sonny. Four it is then. Time to make an effort, time to show Sonny they might have been in the same class once – but not any longer.

Thanks, Phil. How's it going?

Keeping a few jumps ahead. Yourself?

Still in the game.

So I see.

Fucking kids tried taking a lend of me. Bunch of Tiny Tots, but I skelped their arses and seen them off goodstyle. Goodstyle. Cheers. The wee bastards.

Cheers, Sonny. I'm with friends, you understand. Catch you next time.

They were standing outside Franco's. Steve and Mike had just headed off somewhere. It was raining and he was talking:

Fucking kangaroos in the toilet, did I tell you?

Keeping a jump ahead, Phil? Aye, you told me.

He was leaning against the wall:

I'm for offski. See you, Sonny.

Which way're ye gang?

Hame.

He's holding onto a rone.

A good night, eh? Friends, and kangaroos.

Which way, Phil? Which way?

Maybe the Sonny twins were only trying to help, but the fucking questions just kept on coming.

Gang hame, I said.

Aye, Phil, but which way're ye gang?

Gang where?

Eh?

Where we gang?

Not me, Phil. You. Which way're ye gang?

Hame, I keep telling you. See, there's a Joe! Grab it!

He'll no stop. One look at you's enough. You can let go the rone now and haud ontae me. Like that time at school, mind?

Mind what?

At the school – when ye tried battering Billy Chambers? Nearly killing him ye were, till I hauled ye off. Ye'd really lost the heid. I'd tae drag you halfway round the playground to get ye calmed down. Mind? Nou, get a guid haud.

Traffic everywhere he turned, and when he turned too soon the streetlights smeared round with him; the pavement and the road kept tripping him into puddles.

Left here, Phil. Mind the step. Keep going. And –

The same traffic, the same puddles, the same streetlights. When he closed his eyes he felt sick. When he opened them he felt worse.

He was leaning against a wet wall. No more traffic, no more puddles, no more streetlights, no more stepping up and stepping down. He could stay there just as he was all night, suit him. Resting, happy as Larry.

All right, Phil?

Fine, Sonny, fine.

Nearly there. Doon the stairs – Yin at a time, eh!

Another wet wall, another rest.

The two of them were standing in the doorway of a large room; the strip-lighting made him close his eyes. But that sweat-smell was enough, that familiar squeak from the wooden floor as they walked across it.

Hame, for the time being anyroad. Some bits and pieces in the back as'll dae for blankets, an ye can doss on yin o these. Nae feather beds but they dae the trick.

One of the rubber exercise-mats seemed to have lifted itself off the ground and was letting him down gently. Just as he was falling asleep he felt Sonny lay something over him.

A laser stab of brightness cut him out of sleep. He turned over – and the room he was in turned over with him. Shadows, half darkness, bars of harsh light, the smell of rubber about turning his stomach; his head viced tight, and then tighter; his eyes being pressed into their sockets. So long as he wasn't sick ...

Where the hell was he? Back at school it smelt like: the school gym to be exact. A gym at any rate – he could make out sets of barbells, some ropes, weights, wall bars and in the corner, like someone who'd exercised himself till there was nothing left, a punchball. And there, a feet across, a mound of towels and dressing-gowns with someone lying underneath, sleeping. A right battered-looking object it was, too. Fucking Sonny, no less: the bruiser and bampot he spent most of life trying to keep clear of. His mouth felt cracked with thirst, his eyes gummed half open, half shut. A real bitch of a hangover was getting itself up to full strength, but he'd survive; he always had so far.

The night before was like a stack of badly developed photographs that had tipped over, and he was glimpsing them as they fell around him: Steve with a fistful of pints, Sonny and his bruises at the bar, a taxi splashing them, Mike's holidays, the kangaroo condom machine, the set of basement stairs down to the gym. He'd been dreaming about Billy Chambers and bouncing his head off the playground just like he'd done on his first day at secondary school.

The older boys had been circling around them, picking off the new arrivals one at a time and giving them a doing. Nothing too rough, but something so they'd remember their first day. He and Billy had been standing back to back, trying to hold out until the bell. They'd no chance, of course. Not when they were made to fight each other instead, and told they'd get a real kicking if they didn't. Every time they stopped they got laid into. He'd ended up on top of Billy, no longer pretending any more, but battering into him as hard as he could while the rest of them cheered him on. They loved it. He'd felt great. That's when Sonny appeared out of nowhere. The fucking cavalry that nobody'd asked for. Same again last night.

He'd been doing all right, hadn't he, until Sonny appeared? A night out with friends, a few drinks and a few laughs, no big deal really. Not really.

Angus Calder

## WRITING AS A SMALL CONNOISSEUR OF PIZZA

The worlds one has gained,
the worlds one has lost,
the corners I've turned,
the coins that I've tossed,
must not all dissolve
like mist
or the ash of the fags I've burned
getting pissed
before you've returned.
Dario's Pizza del Mare – I
respect gamberetti,
don't charge through the vino,
regain my resolve,
re-encounter the sky,
meet light snow like confetti
wherever you've been, oh.

## BREAD STREET

Is also the street of nan
and pizza
and posho.
Its name represents where
people meet,
that promenade
of Scotlandesh,
where we must andare al spasso,
person with person,
you and me, dear,
under whatever sun.

## JUST OFF LOTHIAN ROAD

Weekends the theatres debouch their crowds
in Grindlay Street, in Cambridge Street

Hibees and Jambos raise their slurry chants
in West Port, in Bread Street

Alone in bed I listen to the sounds
of life outside, in Spittal Street

Imagination takes me far away
to Lawley Road, to Miguel Street

Maoilios Caimbeul

## THAR NA STARSNAICH

Thar na starsnaich
le sunnd, le aighear,
airson gum faca mi boillsgeadh beag
dhen ghrian tro na cùirtearan.
Tha mi a' dol air an t-slighe
le teagamh, le eagal,
airson nach eil mi cinnteach dè tha romham,
no air mo chùlaibh
ged a chunnaic mi aiteal òir air a' bheinn mhaireannaich.

O iodhalan boga na cluasaig!
Tha mi a' gabhail slàn leibh
gu sunndach, le teagamh, le deòir
airson cho ceàrr 's a bha mi cho fada,
airson nan làithean strùidheil,
airson nan cuibhrigean blàth, meallta.
O, a chridhe lèirsinnich!
O, a chridhe shalaich, chealgaich!
Tha thu air do mharbhadh le ìobairt,
air d' fheannadh le sgian na maidne.

Ach theirig thar na starsnaich, na seall air ais
dhan dachaigh bhlàth, chofhurtail
no ris na ballachan dìonach.
Tha thu a-muigh anns an t-solas;
tha na beanntan ag èigheach;
tha na fàsaichean iongantach fa do chomhair;
tha na reultan sìorraidh a' spreadhadh an cuid driùchd ort,
iad co-shìnte ris a' chòmhnard shuthain.
O, iongantais! O, iolaich! O, a mhìorbhail neo-chrìochnaicht'!

Myles Campbell

## OVER THE THRESHOLD

I go over the threshold
joyfully, elated
because I have seen a little gleam
of sunshine through the curtains.
I'm going on a journey
doubtful, tearful,
because I'm not sure what's ahead
or behind me
although I did see a golden gleam on the everlasting mountain.

O soft idols of the pillow!
I take my leave of you
joyfully, with doubt, with tears,
because I have been wrong for so long,
for the spendthrift days,
for the warm, deceitful bedcovers.
O, all-seeing heart!
O deceiving, soiled heart,
you are killed with sacrifices,
flayed by the knife of the morning!

But go over the threshold, don't look back
to the warm comfortable home,
or to the watertight walls.
You are out in the light;
the mountains are shouting;
the marvellous wilderness is before you;
the eternal stars are spraying you with dew,
stretched out with the endless plain.
O marvel! O elation! O unending miracle!

Stuart B. Campbell

## GHANDRUNG

It's the Bowmore ceilidh night!
I am transported:
it's Islay, I am seven years old and smiling,
gormless at the Gaelic, taken in by my clan,
I am carried away:
it's the Ghandrung ceilidh night!

School choirs, mouth-music, the village chanter,
tartan shawls (even Campbell tartan!) the homespun
soprano and the dominie declaring,
'The song of the story is ...'
In Gaelic, in Nepali, in translation
for the sassenachs, for the sahibs.
Sing-along-songs, dancing, unattainable in-jokes,
('There was a Sherpa, a porter and a
climbing expedition ...')
more dancing, drinks from
the (illicit?) rakshi still.

Fortified, the village chancer, thinking himself
Erchie (or the equivalent) sings and dances
'Maggie Lauder' (or the equivalent) mostly for
the blond Dutch smatcher:
front row; all legs and innocence.
After the song Erchie says to her,
'Dae ye want tae come up tae ma bit an see
Ma yak-wool carpet collection?'
(you know your equivalent)
and the Dutch girl smiles,
the only way it's safe
at ceilidhs; things happen and
it's best just to smile.

Stewart Conn

## MONSIEUR BOUZOU

Marcilhac is on the north bank of the Célé, a tributary of the Lot. Stopping at a roadside *auberge* and leaving our bicycles in the shade, we enjoyed a lunch which began with a rich *terrine du pays* and ended with fruit and coffee. Our main objective was the Benedictine abbey. Its Romanesque nave is open to the sky. Only a squat tower stands, its walls overgrown. The Gothic section, rebuilt in the XVth-century in flamboyant style, has carved wooden panels, frescos and coats of arms. In the XIIth-century chapter house are sculptured capitals depicting faces with celestial smiles and mythical animals, half monster and half demon, subjecting the lost souls of sinners to appalling punishment.

From a flight of steps overlooking the south portal I became aware of two distinct and separate bursts of activity. In front of me two elaborately clad tourists were taking photographs. Not indiscriminately, or casually, but with great fixity of intent. The male wore a fore-and-aft cap and despite the warmth, a beige cape. The clicks of his camera were punctuated by lengthy sightings and elaborate refocusings. Intermittently he'd give a wheezy sigh of what I interpreted as aesthetic satisfaction.

His female companion was short and stocky. She had a bigger camera with an electronic zoom lens. She'd confront each object of her attention (or obsession) in a series of feints, like a flyweight boxer; nipping in to catch the unsuspecting stonework unawares, then withdrawing before the figure on it could retaliate. The only sounds, other than the scliff of shoes on the stone flags of the courtyard, were sharp intakes of breath and a sporadic *'Ja'* or *'Jawohl!'*

Her rate of strike must have been three times that of her husband, round whom she would zigzag dexterously, somehow never clashing with his shutter-movements. As I watched, she completed one spool and in the twinkling of an eye was onto another; pointing out to him the base of what to my eye could have been any pillar round any of a hundred now ruined Romanesque abbeys. But they took it from all angles, she finally with knees bent, peering up at it as though it were the foot of some elephantine creature she was stalking.

At this point I realised I wasn't the only observer. Just inside the portal a small, unkempt figure kept appearing round the wooden half door. From where I stood the face seemed undefined, not due to the shadow but because the features themselves seemed to be working away, the mouth and eyes never still. The garb might have been that of a monk, or some member of the clergy. Clearly a functionary of the abbey, he seemed to find the antics of

the photographers as fascinating as I did. Glancing up he moment-
arily caught my eye and disappeared instantly into the darkness
behind the half door. For a few minutes, nothing. Then he would
make tiny forays, flitting out and in like a lizard's tongue so speed-
ily you wondered if you'd seen it at all.

With a final flurry the German pair gathered up their equip-
ment, and went. Instantly the little figure darted from the
doorway, and gestured to us. We headed for the portal. Rather
than speak he pointed, to the accompaniment of disjointed croaks,
at a placard beside the entrance. On it was a speckled newspaper
article, describing how he – M. Jean Bouzou – was the abbey
guide. And as a deaf-mute, communicated with his hands. He
pointed at this, at himself – and held out a hand for the requisite
ten-francs entry payment. Inside he led us to a side table on which
leaflets were stacked and unerringly handed us – out of a selection
which included French and German – the one in English. He
pointed to the numbered paragraphs on the leaflet, indicating in
which direction each described section lay.

Where he thought we'd missed some significant detail or failed
to pay due attention to the carved oakwork, he delicately
impressed himself upon us. The sounds he made had a plaintive-
ness to them – and if it wasn't fanciful, conveyed an affection for
the building. I wondered how he'd picked out the correct leaflet.
Could he lip-read? Even without that, easy I suppose. Given the
extent to which we flaunt our national characteristics. Then we
took in that we were hearing music. An organ was playing. A
choir joined in. For a moment we were startled, at the thought of
our visit coinciding with a mass. Then we realised it was, of
course, on tape. To add to the uncanniness, there was no organ in
the building.

A further irony lay in our guide's role including switching on
and off the ghostly music he could not himself hear. Its conclusion
coincided with the end of our tour. Sensing he was unlikely to pick
up any expression of appreciation I might make, I spontaneously
clasped his hand, shook it firmly ... and stepped out into the sun.

*

We walked alongside the local mill-lade, past clouds of frantically
copulating dragonflies. I mused about our little guide, attributing
to him both a timeless quality and something I couldn't quite
define, but of a period prior to our own. Later, looking up from
unpadlocking our bicycles, I noticed the German couple. Rather
than enter the church, they had commandeered a wooden table at
the edge of a picnic site – but were still energetically photographing
the building and its architecture.

As we rode back along the Célé we slowed down to look at the house frontages of the nearby hamlet of Corn. The war memorial, topped by its heavy grey stone cross, was like any other. But something caught my eye, and I stopped. It was an inscription which not only occupied my mind for the remainder of the cycle run, but continues to do so, with its unresolved possibilities and implications; and its reminder of our abbey guide. Chiselled out were the words: '*à André Bouzou: pris 12 maï, 1944, par les allemands … mort Nov. 1945, âge 19: Bergen-Belsen*'.

24

Anna Crowe

## CAT AND WATER

Our thirsty cat is in the bath
lapping the puddle that squats around the plug-hole.
I turn the tap on slowly –
letting out a steady stream
but not enough to startle her.
She drinks and drinks as though she'll never stop.
Then sits up to watch the water.

It falls in a single uninterrupted flow.
A rapier you'd swear was welded metal
from tap to drain.
Or a glassy rope for a glassy snake to climb.
Mysterious, sinister, thin.
The cat replies to her own unspoken question
and probes it with a forepaw.

O now the sword's a shoal of plunging fish
and smallfry jitterbug off shrugged fur.
Again and again
her claws comb and card it like yarn,
unravelling it in twigs and sprays of light.
She frays the rope in a scatter of seeds
or sways it to a whispery rush of sound.

She knows
what we forget.
She knows this stuff's alive.
Dear beautiful prey to be caught and held and let go and held again.
And when I turn off the tap and she quits the bath
she leaves by way of a blackberry-path of her own.

David Cunningham

# DE MORTUIS

My father and I never really talked, at least not until he died; after he died he wouldn't shut up.

I wasn't there when he died. I was working in the local news-agent. I had left school and was half way through what was widely referred to as my 'gap year'. Since I had no idea what I wanted to do next this seemed a rather optimistic description of it. It felt more chasmal than gap-like to me.

I'd like to be able to say that I sensed him going, that as I walked home for lunch along the promenade I felt a part of myself being irretrievably lost. But I didn't.

Before leaving the promenade I stepped onto the sea wall for a moment. The ocean heaved and thrashed, as if fulminating against the obdurate stillness of the land. The wind, a heady mixture of salt-spray and liberated ozone, streamed through my hair and filled me with a fleeting sense of elation.

*You'll catch your death standing there,* he said.

It was then I knew he had gone.

When I got back to the flat I discovered I was right. Our front room, with its broad view of the Firth of Clyde, was sparsely popu-lated by mismatched figures – my mother, my aunt, the doctor, a district nurse – like a chess board on which a draw should long ago have been declared. They all clutched steaming mugs and gazed out of the windows, as if immobilised by the mesmeric power of the storm. Barely noticed, I slipped past them and went into his room.

He lay in bed on his side. His face was a picture of repose, no longer contorted by the pain of bed sores or the emetic effects of too many drugs.

I bade him a tentative farewell in my thoughts. It was more a vague gesture than anything articulate, but he seemed to under-stand.

*I'm still here you know. You're not getting rid of me that easily.*

His voice resounded inside my head, penetrating and unignor-able. I tried to stay calm and not to yield to my first instinct, which was to run from the room.

'Are you ... ?'

*As a doornail.*

'Oh ... so how does it feel?'

*It's bearable, though I can't seem to see very much. Have they gone?*

'The others? Yes.'

*Thank Christ for that. Your aunt was trying to coax some kind*

*of death-bed repentance out of me, getting me to say that I was
ready to make peace with everyone …*
    'And are you?'
    *The hell I am. You tell her that.*
    'How can I? You're supposed to be dead.'
    *Oh I am dead, son. I most certainly am.*

That was our first conversation and, for a while, I hoped it would
be our last. But he remained a tirelessly voluble presence inside my
head over the next few days.
    They passed quickly in a tumult of wind, rain and hasty funeral
preparations. Friends and neighbours arrived bearing flowers:
freesias, carnations, white lilies, even a tuberose. The flowers
were distributed around the flat and filled it with a cloying scent
that hung like anaesthetic.
    His brothers – to whom he didn't speak after an obscure argu-
ment about the division of their mother's property – turned up
one by one to condole awkwardly with us.
    *Probably want to stick a pin in me to make sure I'm dead.*

'It's so foolish that we never talked all those years. But I suppose
those sorts of things happen in families,' said his tweedy eldest
brother – a solicitor in Galloway – perched on the edge of our sofa.
    My mother and I stared numbly into our cups, hollow-eyed
from lack of sleep and all the arrivals and departures throughout
the day. We murmured vague assent.
    *So does incest and fratricide. But that doesn't excuse them.*
    'I mean I did try to get on with him when we were younger.'
    *All you ever got on was my nerves.*
    'Only we were never really interested in the same things.'
    *On the contrary, we were both interested in ourselves.*
    Snorting, I stood up and excused myself in a strangulated voice.
'He's upset,' I heard my mother saying as I left the room.

With my aunt he was gentler, but still mocking. Towards my mother
he seemed ambivalent.
    At forty-four she was tall and still slim, with the grey hardly
visible in her fine blond hair. Theirs had never – as far as I could
remember – been an especially happy marriage. A civil engineer,
he had worked abroad, in the Far East, a good deal when I was
younger. Even when he returned permanently an emotional distance between them persisted. They shared the same bedroom but
slept in single beds. I noticed that even before I understood what
it meant. As I grew older there was a pervading atmosphere of
indifference in the flat. But, for my sake, they managed to avoid
confrontation, more or less.

When he fell ill she devoted herself to his care and their intimacy seemed to be renewed. But now he treated all her remarks with mordant irony, particularly if they referred to her relationship with me. At such times I wished I could stop up my ears against him. True, I was close to my mother – much closer than to him – but only because he had been absent for so large a part of my childhood. His constant insinuations that she was possessive were like a impugning tide, eroding the foundations on which my life was based. I resented them all the more because, at times, I had suspected her myself.

But his most extraordinary comments were reserved for Alison. Soulful, short-sighted Alison was my friend from school. Walking home from our sixth-year English class, we used to talk about our favourite writers. She was the only person I knew who found books sexy the way most people our age found music sexy. I found her sexy, but she went out with someone else. I avoided referring to him when we talked. So, I noticed, did she. I wasn't altogether surprised when they split up.

Then Dad fell ill. Though I told her and thought she was sympathetic, I feared that turning any of her supportive hugs into a more intimate embrace would shatter what illusions she might cherish about me as a sensitive literary type.

I phoned her the day he died. She came over the day after that and we went for a walk along the beach. The wind continued to blow but the rain had eased and the impenetrable knot of cloud had loosened slightly, admitting short bursts of sunlight which fell on the turbid green ocean and the tousled marram grass. When we returned from our walk we carried on talking in the front room.

'Will you and your mother be able to stay here?' asked Alison, squinting at me.

'Probably not.'

'How's she coping?'

*Struggling to contain her relief at my untimely demise.*

'Pretty well. I think she feels a little bit guilty that they weren't closer in the last few years. I think perhaps she wonders if she could have tried harder.'

*Ha!*

Alison nodded. She knew about the problems in their marriage. Her own parents were separated.

'Well, she must be glad at least that you're still around.'

I always felt vaguely ashamed when Alison referred to my relationship with my mother, as if the fact that we had a relationship at all reflected discredit upon us both and made me ineligible as a lover.

'I suppose she is.'

'Will you go away to college at all now?'

'I don't see why not.'

'No, I only meant that she'll be on her own now if you do. And in a strange house probably. Unless of course she meets someone else.'

I shrugged. It had never occurred to me that she might meet someone else. Now that she was a widow I imagined her future as solitary and celibate: a small semi and a small car, a part-time job, female friends and aqua aerobics. There was silence while Alison and I pondered the implications of what she had said.

*She's a very attractive girl you know.*

'Thank you. I am aware of that.'

*Don't be so defensive. I just wondered if you'd noticed.*

'I'm not being defensive and yes I had noticed.'

*So why haven't you done anything about it?*

'Well it's complicated. I mean we're friends.'

*It's not complicated. It's simple.*

'Look, can't you give us some privacy. Close your eyes?'

*I don't have eyes, son, I'm dead. Sans eyes, sans teeth.*

'Well can't you do anything?'

*No, I can't do anything. Not any more. But you can. And I'd want to fuck that girl if I were you.*

'Dad!' I exclaimed, aloud this time.

Startled from her reverie, Alison looked up. I stared back at her, open mouthed. Then, in a sublime gesture of misinterpretation, she hastened to my side and put her arms around me. I held her close for longer than I had ever allowed myself to before. She felt tender and pliant as a sapling.

'It's OK,' she murmured.

I could think of nothing to say, but mumbled into her shoulder in a tone which betokened distress.

He chuckled.

*Don't say I never do anything for you.*

The funeral may be briefly described. It took place in weather so foul that it was hastened through by all those concerned – apart from my dad obviously – with an eagerness just short of disrespectful. While the chiaroscuro of sunshine and shower persisted, around the graveside umbrellas congregated tightly, like a cluster of toadstools.

*Look at them,* he said. *Can't wait to get it over with.*

'It's freezing,' I pointed out.

The coffin sat on planks of wood, laid breadthwise across the grave. I, my aunt and two of my uncles were called over to manage its final descent. I grasped a cord. The rain drummed on the lid, like bored fingertips.

The planks were slid away and the sudden weight, evenly distributed between the four of us, was arresting.

*It's all right. Take the strain,* he said.

I took the strain. The grave gaped obscenely, a black slot in the earth. The coffin lurched downwards into it. Just before it was swallowed up the sunlight burst upon it and created a sparkling aureole around the lid.

*Isn't that beautiful? If I had eyes I could weep.*

Afterwards everyone reconvened damply in our front room. The greater his relatives' estrangement from him had been, the more stridently they expressed their sense of loss. I passed amongst them with pots of tea and coffee. As I did so he dished the dirt on each person: how she had slept with her sister's husband, how he had nearly been caught for tax evasion, how they had an unhealthy attachment to their dog.

Finally it was too much for me and I fled the room. The doctor, who had come along, prescribed a sedative. (My mother had already been given one.) I was fed a huge volume of warm milk and packed off to bed.

The soporific effect of the pills was counteracted by the ache of my over-full bladder and, late at night, when they had all gone, I stumbled woozily up the hall to the bathroom and thence to the dark front room.

The windows of the flat below threw squares of light onto the lawn. The tide had retreated from the glossy ridges of sand, but the wind continued to howl.

*Enjoy it while you can.*

'You're still there? I was wondering.'

*Yes, I'm still here. Just. I want to tell you before I go how I feel about you.*

'How do you feel about me?' I asked, genuinely curious. He had offered few clues on this topic during his life.

*I love you – you know that.*

'Do I?'

*Look, I'm trying to make amends here. I know you feel there was a distance between us when you were younger because I was never interested in who you were.*

'There was a distance between us because you were in Malaysia.'

*Granted. But I was in Malaysia because I loved my work and wanted to do well. Not because I didn't love you, whatever your mother might have told you.*

'She never …'

*No, she never said it outright. But every time I came back I was more of an intruder between you and her. I abandoned her – so she thought – just like her father did. So you became her mainstay, her company. When I came back there wasn't a role for me any more. I know it was mostly my fault. But now that I'm gone it's going to get worse if you don't get away.*

'You can't just ...'

*You can't be her crutch. You've been patted on the head today for being a good son by people who haven't given a moment's thought to what will happen to you now. They've probably made you feel like you're a man. But you're not. You're still a boy, scared of the big, bad world. So you'll use the fact that she needs you to stay at home. But she's not your responsibility. She's an adult. She's her own responsibility. And you're allowing yourself to be smothered by her. You know you are. Don't tell me I'm wrong.*

I squirmed, covered in a hot pelt of embarrassment, but he was relentless.

*What about that girl?*

'Alison.'

*Alison, yes. Don't you want her?*

'But we're just friends ...'

*Don't make excuses.*

I put my hands over my ears.

*You can't shut me out, son. Of course you love your mother. She's kind and gentle and intelligent and she's always been there when you've needed her – unlike me. But she'll cut your balls off if you let her and the trouble it'll store up for both of you later won't be worth living for. You'll wake up one morning in ten years' time and realise that you've forfeited your life. And then you'll hate and resent her and she won't be able to understand why.*

In a frenzy – but still disoriented from the pills – I began to unlock all the windows to drown him out. I wrenched them open one by one, admitting a ferocious wind that grew stronger by degrees. Photographs, many sepia tinted (unearthed by my mother that morning), spun through the air like so many autumn leaves. Lamp-shades spun and tilted crazily. Plants toppled, spilling soil over the carpet. The shouting pungency of the ocean filled the room.

At that moment my mother, hair streaming, entered the room. She found me standing motionless in the middle of the darkened floor. With her silk-print robe drawn round her and the wind plucking at the hem of her night-dress, she looked like an insomniac Lady of Shallott. Somewhere in the recesses of the flat a door was slammed heavily by the hurtling air.

'David, what's going on?' she asked, not unreasonably.

There was nothing I could tell her, nothing I could explain. I closed the windows and the chaos subsided. Together we tidied the room. Though she asked me again several times what was wrong, all I could say was, 'I'm sorry.' She said we would talk in the morning.

We did talk in the morning. But now that he had put all my vague apprehensions of her neediness into words I found it impossible to be honest with her. My natural impulse was to reach out to her in her perplexity. But I felt an equally strong impulse to recoil from her. So I tried to hold myself aloof.

The storm had blown itself out, my aunt had left and an uncertain silence prevailed in the flat.

In the afternoon, as we were sorting through his clothes, my mother said: 'I hope you don't feel in some way you have to be responsible for me now.'

At first I thought he was using her to perform some perverse act of ventriloquism. But as she continued I realised that these were her words:

'I've lost my husband. Whatever went wrong between us in the last few years it's still terribly sad and I'll miss him very much. But you've lost your father, and that's much worse. Life's so much harder when you don't have a father to support you and help you along. And that's all the more reason why you have to be able to enjoy your life and do what you really want with it, regardless of how I feel. You're my son. I don't expect you to be my surrogate husband as well.'

'But that means you'll be alone,' I said.

She smiled sadly.

'Darling, I've been alone for some time now. I'm used to it.'

I nodded.

'Did you hear that?' I asked him.

*Yes. Yes I heard.*

She went out that evening to visit a neighbour and Alison came over. We shared a bottle of red wine left over from the day before. In my room I talked about myself and about us and told her what my mother had said. She listened and sipped her wine, gazing at me over the rim of her glass. I confessed all my fears, though not that it was my dead father who had given voice to them. The wine I drank, and my exponentially increasing frankness, closed the brief distance between us. I must admit I used her sympathy as leverage in easing her towards my bed. But when she folded herself against me and I melted into her none of that – or anything else – seemed to matter.

Later we clung together. It was dark, and so quiet that I could hear my pulse. But there was a vacancy in the darkness too.

'Are you still there?' I asked.

There was no reply.

Jenni Daiches

## MEN AT NIGHT

A gap in the curtains brings in a slice of moon.
I lie and think of men. How so many cast
a light upon themselves, oblivious of the shadows,
and call in blistered voices for attention. How
they carry war with women in their heads and lose
their hearts to threats of challenge.
                              There are exceptions.
My companion sleeps with a hand on my shoulder,
as if I might flit or fade or melt.
The moon walks on my wall as I lie in the dark.

**Robert Davidson**

## STRATHCLYDE CONCERTO #9
**for six woodwind instruments**
*(by Peter Maxwell Davis)*

Pale light spilling across the tidal race;
long night turns to dawn, day will follow soon.
A croft house window with four dusty panes;
lined paper on a desk, an empty room.
 *Piccolo, alto flute and cor anglais;*
 *two clarinets and a contrabassoon.*

November's limpid dawn travels this way;
over Hoy and Stromness, the Maeshowe tomb.
Clouds gleam like silver, then fade into grey.
The sun shares the sky with the fading moon.
 *Piccolo, alto flute and cor anglais;*
 *two clarinets and a contrabassoon.*

The Orkney Isles are picked out in detail
as only this low-angled light can do;
the grain in the rock, sparkle of the waves,
lichen-covered stones with battle-axe runes.
 *Piccolo, alto flute and cor anglais;*
 *two clarinets and a contrabassoon.*

Music does this too, makes the common rare;
as memory brings them back real and new,
the lost, the dead, the one who went away,
the choir of the gone in the empty room.
 *Piccolo, alto flute and cor anglais;*
 *two clarinets and a contrabassoon.*

Darkness slowly falls and day flees this place;
cold night and silence fasten on the moor.
Frost blossoms on the runes like burning lace,
a lone, clear voice intones the final tune.
 *Piccolo, alto flute and cor anglais;*
 *two clarinets and a contrabassoon.*

**Martin Donnelly**

## ONE DRUNKEN NIGHT

well as I went home on a monday night
as drunk as drunk could be
I saw a horse outside the door
where my old horse should be.
well I called my wife and I said to her,
'will you kindly tell to me ...'
and she said, 'you're fucked; get to bed.'

I went to bed.

Anne Donovan

## A CHITTERIN BITE

We'd go tae the baths every Saturday mornin, Agnes and me. Ah'd watch fae the windae, alang the grey, gluthery street, till ah caught the first glimpse of her red raincoat and blue pixie hat turnin the corner, then ah'd grab ma cossie, wrap it up in the bluegrey towel, washed too many times, and heid for the door.

*Ah'm away, Mammy.*

Ma mammy would appear fae the kitchen, haudin a wee bundle, wrapped up in the waxed paper fae the end of the loaf.

*Here you are, hen, your chitterin bite.*

Inside were two jammy pieces, wan for me and wan for Agnes, tae eat efter the swimmin on the way alang the road, a chitterin bite, no enough tae fill your belly, just somethin tae stave aff the chitterin cauld when you come oot the baths.

The noise hits you the minute you open that big green door; the ceilin high and pointy like a chapel roof, makin everythin echo roon its beams. It leaks, so drips of watter plash on your heid while you're swimmin. The place is fulla weans, screechin at their pals ower the racket. Two boys are leppin in fae the side till big Alex blaws his whistle and threatens tae pap them oot. There's a row a boxes at each side of the pool, the hauf doors painted bright blue, the left-haun side for the women and the right for the men. Agnes and me get changed in the wan cubicle; her cossie has blue ruched bits aw roon, while mines is yella wi pink flooers. You can just see the two wee bumps startin tae grow on her chist and she footers aboot, sortin her straps tae try tae cover them.

*Whit dae they feel like?*

*You can touch them if you want.*

Ah push two fingers gently intae her left breist which goes in a wee bit under the pressure.

*Is it sore?*

*Naw, disnae feel like anythin really.*

Ah look doon at ma ain chist, totally flat. Ma mammy says ah'll be next but ah cannae imagine it.

*C'mon, let's get a move on, ah'm freezin.*

We run oot the cubicle and plunk straight intae the watter, the shock of the cauld makin us scream as usual. Ah hate jumpin intae the baths but ah love it as well.

I still go swimming, but now to the warm and brightly lit leisure centre with its saunas and steam rooms, aromatherapy massages and hot showers. Tuesday is Ladies Night and I drive there in my

car; shampoo, conditioner and body lotion neatly tucked in my
designer sportsbag along with a change of clothing. Dressed-up
clothing; short skirt, sheer tights and silky shirt.

Afterwards I meet Matthew in the Italian restaurant, an anony-
mous place tucked away in a side street. We are unlikely to be
spotted here for there are several places with cheaper food and
more atmosphere in the area, so Matthew and I have made it our
own. As I push open the door I see he is sitting at our usual table,
his head bent over the menu, dark shiny hair neatly slicked back
with gel. He looks up as I cross the room and I feel my breath
catch in my throat.

He goes to the gym on Tuesdays before he comes to meet me so
we're both showered, powdered and squeaky clean. I breathe in
the sweet scent of his aftershave and the clean soapy smells of his
body. His lips graze my cheek but I am aware that his eyes scan
the room, just in case anyone is watching. I sit opposite him, feeling the thick white tablecloth under my hands, knowing we both
look good in the pinkish glow of the candlelight. I finger the heavy
wine glass, rolling the stem between my thumb and index finger,
sipping delicately.

The cauld hits you as soon as you're ootside, efter the heavy door
sclaffs shut. Oor hair is soakin, plastered tae wer heids and wee
dreeps run doon the back of yer neck. Ma mammy says put your
pixie on efter the swimmin or you'll get a cauld in the heid, but
that just makes it worse, the damp seeps through tae you feel your
brain's frozen up inside. Agnes and me walk, airms linked, stuffin
dauds a breid intae wer mooths. Ma mammy saves us the big
thick enders that you sink yer teeth intae, the raspberry jam runnin oot and tricklin doon yer chin. Ah wipe it away wi the endy
the damp towel.

The cafe is two streets away. The windaes are aye steamed up
so you cannae see in and the name, *Bellini's*, is printed above the
door in fancy red letters. As you push open the heavy doors, heat
whaps you that hard it's like bein slapped roon the face, and yer
heid starts tae tingle. The cafe is divided up intae booths, each wi
gless panels, frosted like sugar icing, so when you're inside wan
you feel you're in yer ain wee world. The seats flip up and doon
on creaky metal hinges and you have tae watch or you catch yer
fingers in them. No that Agnes and me sit in the booths very
often. We hardly ever have enough money for a sit-in. Usually we
just get a cone or a bag of sweeties. But in the winter the smell of
chips and the steam risin fae the frothy coffee makes your belly
feel that empty.

Agnes and me pool wer money, leavin aside what we need tae
get intae the pictures.

*What'll we get – midget gems?*
*We got them last week – whit aboot cherry lips?*
*Aye, quarter a cherry lips, please.*
Cherry lips are ma favourites: they're harder than midget gems
but wi a funny taste tae them, wersh almost, no like any other
sweeties. But the best thing is their shape; they're like wee smiley
mooths aboot an inch wide an if you sook in yer ain lips and stick
a cherry wan on tap it looks dead funny. Sometimes me n Agnes
dae that an kid on we're kissin, just like at the pictures. Agnes
crosses her eyes and makes me laugh and the cherry lips fall oot.

Affairs have their own rules, unspoken, unwritten, which soon
become engraved on your heart.
1. Never go anywhere you are likely to be seen together.
2. Never show affection in public.
3. Never mention his wife.
4. Never cry.
5. Never phone him at home.
6. Never give your name if you phone him at work.
7. Never whinge if he has to cancel a meeting.
8. Never tell your friends about him.
9. Never leave marks on him.
It would be more satisfying if there were ten rules but I can't
think of another.

I just broke the last rule. I can see the purply red mark, about an
inch across, nestling just above his left shoulder blade, where he
won't see it, but she will. I didn't do it deliberately, but what does
that mean? I knew I was sooking a wee bit harder than I usually
do, for a wee bit longer, yes. I wasn't really sinking my teeth into
him with force, I couldn't tell it was going to leave a mark, not for
sure. Guilty or not guilty? I lean, propped up on my elbow, and
watch him, sleeping, lying on his right side, dark whispers of hair
fanning across the white sheets, like an ad for some expensive per-
fume. Soon he will wake and I will watch him putting on his
clothes which now lie neatly over the chair, he will kiss me without looking into my eyes and I will close the door on him and
stand, listening as his footsteps echo down the hallway.

We go tae the pictures every week efter the swimmin, scramblin tae
get the chummy seats up the back, sharin wer sweeties, grabbin
each other's airms at the scary bits and gigglin at the love scenes.
Then wan week, when we're walkin alang the road efter the baths,
Agnes says:
*Ah said we'd meet Jimmy McKeown and his pal at the pictures.*
*What?*

*He wants tae go wi me. He says he'll bring his pal for you.*
*Do you want tae go wi him?*
*Ah don't know, ah'll gie it a try.*
Ah unlinked ma airm fae Agnes's and marched on, starin ahead.
*Well you don't need me tae come too.*
Agnes caught up wi me, grabbin at ma airm.
*Ah canny go masel.*
*How no?*
*Ah just canny. Anyway, he's bringin his pal. If you don't go ah canny go, come on, Mary, be a pal.*
The boys are waitin for us inside the foyer of the picture hoose. Jimmy McKeown is a year aulder than us, wi a broad nose, a bit bent tae the side, and straight dirty-fair hair in a side shed. The pal is staunin hauf behind him, a wee skinny laddie wi roond baby cheeks and red lips like a lassie.
*This is Shuggie, he's ma cousin.*
*This is Mary.*
*Hiya.*
*Will we go in?*
*After youse, girls.*
They're polite, even though Jimmy is actin the big shot and the pal still hasny opened his mooth. Agnes and me go first, intae the daurk picture hoose, Agnes leadin the way tae the back row where the chummy seats are. She sits doon in wan but when ah go tae sit next tae her she mutters *Naw, you huvty sit wi Shuggie* and shoves me ower tae the next seat, where the airm rest forms a barrier between me and her. Ah feel Shuggie's knees pushin intae mines as he squeezes by me tae sit in the other hauf of the seat. Ah move as far ower tae the side nearest Agnes that ah can, but ah canny help smellin the rough hairy smell of his sports jaicket under the sourness of the aftershave he must of plastered on his baby cheeks.

I don't expect the phone call. Not so soon anyway, not at work, not at ten o'clock in the morning, sitting at my bright shiny desk with my red folder in front of me and my bright shiny, perfectly modulated work voice:
*Good morning, Mary Henderson speaking, how may I help you?*
*Mary? It's me, Matthew, listen, I've got to talk to you, it's urgent. Can you meet me for lunch?*
*Of course.*
*Look, I can't talk now. Can you meet me, in Sarti's? One o'clock?*
*OK. Make it quarter to though, you know how busy it gets there.*
*Right. See you then.*

*

At lunchtime Sarti's is full of people in suits from nearby offices
and the atmosphere is warm and faintly smoky. We sit down at a
table just opposite the deli counter, which is piled high with different kinds of *panettone*. Matthew looks immaculate in his grey suit
and silk floral tie, but as he bends his head to look at the menu I
see a few stray bristly hairs, just where his cheekbone joins his
neck, which he must have missed when shaving this morning. He
looks at the menu as he speaks.
  *What are you having?*
  *Spaghetti vongole, I think. I'm starving. Maybe a night of pas-*
*sion makes you hungry.*
  He looks up but does not smile.
  *I don't have time for lunch, I think I'll just have coffee and a bit*
*of cake.*
  *A chitterin bite.*
  *What?*
  *It's what we used to call a bite to eat, not a full meal, just*
*enough to keep the cold out after the swimming.*
  He folds the menu up and replaces it in its holder.
  *Speaking of bites …*
  I look him straight in the eyes.
  *Mary, do you know what kind of a mark you left on me last*
*night?*
  *Did I?*
  He squeezes his left hand tight into a fist, then releases it, repeat-
ing the movement several times as though it were an exercise.
  *She went berserk when she saw it.*
  *What did you tell her?*
  *I must have bruised myself at the gym, crap like that. How the*
*hell do you bruise yourself on the shoulder blade? I'm sure she*
*doesn't believe me but I think she's accepted it.*
  *That's good.*
  *For heaven's sake couldn't you be more careful?*
  *Must have been carried away by passion I suppose.*
  *You don't seem to be all that concerned about it.*
  *I'm not the one that's cheating on my wife.*

We never spoke aboot it, Agnes and me, though as the week pro-
gressed a cauldness grew between us, a damp seepin cauld like
the wan that gets intae your bones when you don't dry yourself
quick enough efter the swimmin. And the next Saturday, when ah
haunded her her piece and jam, she shook her heid and looked
away fae me.
  *Naw thanks, Mary, ah said ah'd meet Jimmy at Bellini's and*
*we're gonny have chips.*

*Oh.*

She put her airm in mines.

*You can come too. It'll be good tae get sumpn hot inside us steidy just a chitterin bite. We'll go tae the pictures efter. Shuggie's no gonny be there, it's OK.*

Ah pulled ma airm free of Agnes's.

*Two's company, three's a crowd. Ah'll see you at school on Monday.*

The sky was heavy and grey and fulla rain. Ah didnae want tae go hame but ah couldny think of where else tae go so ah wandered roon the streets, gettin mair and mair droukit, no really payin any heed tae where ah was goin, till ah fund masel ootside Bellini's. Ah cooried doon in a close on the other side of the street and watched the door till ah seen them come oot. Agnes was laughin as Jimmy held the door open for her. Their faces were pink wi the heat and Agnes's hair had dried noo, intae wee fuzzy curls aw ower her heid. They set aff towards the pictures, him cairryin her towel under his airm. Ah unwrapped ma piece and took a bite. The breid was hard and doughy and as ah chewed it didny seem tae saften, so the big lumps stuck in ma throat. Ah stood up and heided for hame. As ah passed the waste grund on the corner, ah flung the pieces tae the birds.

*I'm sorry, Mary, I think it would be better if we didn't see each other for a while.*

*A while?*

*She's going to be suspicious, she'll be watching my every move at the moment. If we wait a few weeks she'll calm down and then we can go back to where we were.*

*Which is?*

*I thought we both knew the score.*

How could I have fallen in love with someone who uses expressions like that, like something out of a bad song. But I had.

*Mary, you know I love you, I really do, but I can't leave her and the kids. I've never pretended I could. What we have together is very precious to me, but if it's not enough for you ...*

Someone opened the door behind us and a cold draught cut through the heat of the restaurant. I looked across at Matthew, so beautiful in his perfect suit, and shook my head.

*No, it's not enough. You're right. We have to end it.*

*I'm sorry.*

*So am I.*

The waitress arrived with Matthew's coffee and piece of *panettone.* He looked at it for a moment, then at me.

*Look, I'm sorry, I don't think I can face this. Do you mind?*

*No, it's OK, on you go.*

He reached across the table and held my hand, squeezing it gently.

*Look after yourself.*

*You too.*

*Look, I really am sorry, I just can't talk just now.*

*It's OK, just go, I'll be fine.*

He stood up and walked past me, brushing against my shoulder on the way out. I stared at the empty seat in front of me.

*Spaghetti vongole?*

*Thank you.*

*Black pepper? And Parmesan?*

She flourished the pepper mill, spooned Parmesan over the dish, then left.

Steam rose from the spaghetti and the clam shells gleamed dully like slate roof tiles. It smelled wonderful and I was starving. I picked up my fork, twirled the pasta round and round, pressing it against the spoon, and ate.

**John Duffy**

# FROM THE MORNING WATCH EVEN UNTIL NIGHT

The Month of the Holy Souls: *Out of the depths*
the whole school sang in the big school hall,
Purgatory pressing their unspoken reproaches down
upon us all. We sang it at Josie Crawford's funeral too,
stared at the whiteness of his coffin, imagined
what he'd turned into, hidden in the dark. He splintered
the factory skylight, fell to crack his skull
on the steel rim of the acid vat, then splashed inside.
The first brutal death of my life.
He'd always scared me, now here was his picture,
huge in The Record. He was dead.
We survived to sing November hymns
for the souls of the faithful departed,
patient amidst the cleansing flames.
He left me an image of thick white stuff
that burns, destroys, then drifted away
from the quick tough flicker of his days.

Rhoda Dunbar

# NEWS

### Science news

Brain-stems (of women)
during pregnancy
shrink
Recovery (of size)
takes time.

### Local news

Two cars collided
and went, as can happen,
on fire. Firemen
released the drivers but
could not reach
a baby
in a cot.

### National news

The mother
(brain-stem shrunk ...) saw only
the child
in the cot
in the flames
through which
(though the firemen, distraught, did try to stop her)
she leapt,
reaching the cot but
dying
several days later
of burns.

### Local news

The child (the cot was of fire-retardant material)
lives, relatively (as far as can be scientifically measured)
unscarred.

### Science news

Brain-stems ...

**R.J. Ford**

## SERIOUSLY

It's the way
when you're straddling me
you can take me in hand
without awkwardness –
the condom's filmy gag
will not divert you,
I am not dumbfounded,
you know our route –
how you can steer
well wide of the years
since we first fumbled,
geared now to tenderness,
the delicate offering
of the opening of moist lips,

today like this:
your buttocks, dropped hint
of labia beneath, dog on dog,
so excited, at half-cock
I might all
come to nothing,

but then you're on top,
I'm propped up
by the gargling washing machine,
economy cycle –

it's no trouble
to turn right over
without disengaging,
laughing out loud
if we do do it
(the skill of it!)
'Look, no mess!',

and mess –

that's the seriousness
I love.

Moira Forsyth

# A WHIM

Drifting round Woolworth
somewhere between stationery and socks
she was gripped by desire, and halted,
waiting for sensation to fade.

Dazed minutes later,
it had thickened so she left
strode to her car, got in,
went straight to his house.

Fresh from his bath tousle-haired
buttoning a cuff, he looked up
surprised, then was flattered
by her mouth hot on his.

More starfish than woman
she writhed, he was tentacled,
till roused, he took command.

Afterwards, drinking coffee
he watched from the window
her car creep down the lane.

Only she, flushed and fuelled,
gathering speed on the road,
knew how small a part he'd played.

Paul Foy

## INTERVIEW WITH A PRODDY VAMPIRE

I want you to go to Transylvania, he says, aw poncy poash like cuz he thinks he's some soart a big shot livin oot in the sooth side in his malky big bungalow like he does noo an callin himself Managing Director.

Is that place no full a Tims? A says back. Whit dae ye need me tae go therr fur anywey, can ye no dae yer business bey fax? But it's aw aboot this bloke, this stupit Count that has boaght a hoose up the Whitecraigs an wants it decorated but he's no goat a fax an's no oan the internet, says, Naw, he's an auld fashioned Count an likes tae dae things face tae face an A've tae go ower therr an draw up the plans wey him fur the interior decoration an he's payin fur the trip an that so that's how A ends up therr.

But it's no easy tae get tae wherr his big hoose is, merr like a big bluddy castle, so he's goney huv tae send his Landrover doon tae pick me up at this wee soart a inn place, ye know, a pub wey a few rooms upsterrs tae stay in if ye git too bevvied tae be able tae make it hame, that soart a thing.

An it's aw dead nice therr in this wee part a the country, like when A gets aff the train the station's aw wee an pokey but dead auld an pictyerskew wey its wee flooers hangin in therr wee basket thingies an big cherrs probably made fae oak or sumthin an aw roon aboot is big hills an mountains, aw green an trees at the boattom, then aw grey an craggy as ye go up a bit, an then a big dod a snow at the top like ye always did in yer drawins a mountains when ye wur at school, an it's no even that cauld. Aw dead pretty an ye can just tell that Tims live here.

An this inn's full a them, aw sittin therr, lookin aboot two centuries oot a date, wummin wey shawls roon therr heids, big long skirts like they wurr made fey curtains, and these things they werr roon therr bodies that make therr tits stick oot. An the men wey the stupit hats wey the feather stickin oot the side, big wooly sideburns coverin half therr coupons. Just like at Parkheid. But whit's the score wey these pint glasses? A mean, the'rr bigger than yur usual pint which is fine by me, but they've gote these wee lids on them like the'rr teapots urr sumthin.

Anywey, A've gote a wee bit time tae kill fore A'm tae get picked up so's, of course, A indulges in a wee bevy, soakin up the local culture so tae speak. No bad beer either. Full bodied stuff, if ye know whit A mean. But A'm no enjoyin mahsel cuz aw these punters urr lookin at me funny an A cin see that the'rr nominatin wan eh them tae be a spokesman fur them cuz the'rr aw soart a pushin this grey an wrinkly wee punter ower tae me an A'm thinkin, A bet they want tae know whit team A support, whether A'm a Tim ur a Proddy, that soart a thing.

So up comes this punter an he says, Where you go? Where you go? an Ah says, Who wants tae know? an he looks roon at aw the others, aw confused, an then repeats, Where you go? Where you go? so's A tells him, A'm waitin tae be picked up tae go tae the Count's place. Well, this auld punter looks like he's gonny cack his pants an then when he tells everywan they aw look like the'rr aboot tae cack therr pants anaw and the'rr pushin and pushin this auld punter right up tae me, gabberin oan like a bunch a wee lassies, and then he starts gaun oan an oan tellin me A've no tae go therr, aw in this shitty broken English, an A tells him A um goan and if he wants tae buy me a pint then that's awright, but if he disnae then wid he mind gettin himself tae buggery. Tae be honest A don't think he gote everythin that A said, but he gote the idea.

Next thing happens, A canny believe mah eyes an A'm really close tae cloutin someb'dy, A cin tell ye. First thing, they aw starts makin the sign eh the croass, like they've scored fur Celtic ur sumthin an A'm aboot tae ask ur they tryin tae take the piss ur what, an if the'rr lookin fur trouble they'll bluddy well get it, when mah jaw nearly wallops me in the bollocks. This auld wummin, this wee wifey wey a moustache hobbles forward and tries tae put a crucifix roon mah neck. Well A'm like, Ur you tryin tae be funny hen? cuz A'm tellin ye, granny ur nae granny, A'll lowp wan oan ye if ye don't git that bloody hing away fae me.

So therr's me staunin therr expectin tae get chibbed but A'm gonny take a few a them wey me when the car horn starts honkin ootside an aw these sheepshaggin local types crap therr kecks for real this time, runnin aboot mental like players in a Queen's Park v Brechin City match. Then the door comes crashin open, aw special effects like, an the'rrs naeb'dy therr cept aw this mist comin in fae the dark like the mountains huv been chain smokin an A knows that's mah cue so's A stands up aw full eh mahsel like we aw know Rangers dominate the league and we aw know who A support. An aff A steps ootside, singin, Hullo, hullo, we are the Billy boys. Ootside tae meet mah destiny.

He's quite a cool punter, smartly dressed in this soart a soaft leather long coat over Calvin Klein jeans and T-shirt. None eh yer Kappa track-suit stuff here. He's staunin next tae this big cus-tomized Landrover, like the alterations huv probably cost merr than the bluddy thing itsel, but if ye've goat money then A sup-pose ye can dae what ye want. An A'm thinkin eh the gaffer back hame and like, Think yu'rr poash dey ye? Then come an check this punter oot, ya manky wee nyaff that ye urr.

Anywey, he introduces himsel, tells me he's the Count an that an A says, Ferr doos, an tells him who A um an he says he knows, an A suppose we both knows but ye huv tae dae the introductions an that. So we've gote the intros over wey an we get in the caur, me sittin next tae him an as he drives aff A starts tae get the first inklin uv a suspicion cuz he disnae say anythin, jist sits therr, gies me a sideways glance an this soart a sickenin smile an A thinks, A hope this bloke isnae wan eh them hoofter types. Whitever, the bloke's a customer, an a rich wan at that so's A've goat tae try an get oan wey him – though if he tries anythin oan wey me A'm gonny bust him an therr's nae way the gaffer cin blame me fur that.

So A says tae him, standard soart a patter an that, Whit soart a school did ye go tae then?

A very private school, he says in this really toaffy voice that ye can tell is snooty even though he's gote this really thick foreign accent which is even thicker than the sheep shaggers in the pub.

Oh aye, who educated ye then? Nuns an that?

Oh no, he says and lets oot this huge laugh like A've said sumthin really funny. No nuns would come anywhere near the school I went to.

So yer no Catholic then? A asks, thinkin A might as well get tae the hert eh the matter.

Dear me no old chap, he says, but no really like that ye understaun. Ye hiv tae realise, A'm makin him sound soart a English upper-class public schoolboay, jist tae gie ye the flavour a whit he wis like. Aw superior like. Imagine that wi a bit a Boris Yeltsin an yiv goat the idea. Anywey, Dear me no, he says, My family was excommunicated many generations ago.

Well that's a relief, A'm thinkin, Ye might be a mattress muncher but at least yer no a Tim. So A tells him aboot the folk in the inn tryin tae get me tae werr a crucifix and he looks a bit uneasy fur a minute an asks if A took it but A reassure him that A'm a blue-nose and he looks relieved and tells me that the people here are a bit backward and hing oan tae these auld superstitious weys and A says that mibbe this place should twin up wey the east end a Glesga.

So wu'rr drivin up the side eh this mountin, up aw these wee windy roads wi big rocks hingin oot like the'rr gonny faw oan ye but they don't an it's aw right really cus this is a smart vehicle the auld Count hus an some mental music system an aw, pity he's listenin tae aw this classical shite. A asks him if he's gote any techno an he says naw he husnae, so A goes intae mah bag an gies him a Ibiza tape tae put oan an he's listenin away an then says somethin weird, like, Ah yes, I think I like this modern music. The beat reminds me of the blood pumping through the veins of a young virgin's arteries, an A says, Ye'll huv a joab findin any virgins oot in Ibiza, an he jist laughs an A'm thinkin he's mibbe no so bad efter aw.

Jist as we arrive at his big castle-like hoose therr's a big flash a lightenin an A think that's quite propriate cuz it makes everythin look like it's in black an white an his hoose looks like it belongs in wan eh them auld black an white fillums oan the telly like the *Addams Family* ur the *Munsters* ur sumthin. Anywey, it looks pretty cool an A canny figure why the Count wid want tae go an live in Whitecraigs, unless mibbe he's Jewish but that's awright wi me, long as we urny importin any merr Tims intae the country.

So he takes me intae the hoose an tells me that the servants ur aw oot fur the night an wu'rr aw alone in the place an A'm thinkin, Oh aye, an Ah'm gettin suspicious again but he says A've no tae worry cuz he's no gonny bite an wid A like a bite cuz before they left he hid the servant prepare a big meal fur me an he shows me intae this big room an therr's aw this poash food laid oot an he says A've tae dig in but A've please tae excuse him cuz he's no hungry an A asks him hus he any bevy an he says whitever ah want an A'm thinkin this'll dae me.

It's a big table wu'rr sittin at wi big candelabras an stuff an A'm pretty glad that he's chosen tae sit up the other end fae me cuz it his be said that his breath is a bit oan the bowfin side. At furst ah'm thinkin it's garlic breath, but ... well, yu'll see aboot that in a bit.

So wu'rr hivin a bit eh a natter an he's sayin how we'll go ower the plans fur his new hoose in the mornin an he's askin me how long A've been a jiner an A says, A'm no a jiner ah'm an interior decorator, an he says, Yes of course, an A'm bein polite an that but no too friendly cuz A don't want tae gie him any ideas. Thinks A, A'll talk tae him aboot the fitba, bit a lads talk, ye know. So's A asks him, When ye go aff tae live in Glesga, an he interupts wey, The suburbs, actually, old chap, an A says, Whitever. When ye move therr, whit team dae ye think ye'll support.

Well who do you support? he asks, an A says, The Gers, of course, an he says, wey a bit eh a wink A don't like, Well that shall do me then, an it's it that point that A'm cuttin intae mah stake which hus the bludd runnin oot eh it when whit dae A go and dae but cut mah bluddy finger an then it has the bludd runnin oot it anaw.

So noo he gets aw funny an his eyes go aw weird an therr's this funny noise comin fae oot his throat, like right deep doon inside, an A'm askin if he's awright when he just comes flyin ower fae the other side eh the table, grabs me – an he's a strong Count – an sticks his bluddy teeth right intae mah neck. A'm like, Get aff a me ya big jobby jabber ye, an he's goin slurp slurp an A'm feelin like a right dick wey is mingin breath aw sleazy aw ower me so's A starts thumpin im right in the temple but A cannae hurt the bugger an he lifts me right up so's mah feet urr aff the groon an kickin aboot tryin tae get his shins ur kneecaps but he jist keeps slurpin away an's no bothered.

Noo he droaps mi an A'm lyin oan the groon wi mah legs aw at funny angles an he's standin ower me wi is eyes aw red an weird lookin, an wi aw the bludd he's drunk fae me he looks like he's gote lipstick oan an A tell im he's claimed. He jist stauns therr wi is hauns oan is hips laughin an says, You should be thankful to me, for I shan't kill you. And you will show your gratitude. Soon the effects of my bite will take effect and you will join the lower ranks of the undead and shall serve me, your master.

Whit urr you oan aboot? ya big tit ye, A says tae him. He says tae me that he's a vampire an A'm gaun tae be joinin him soon an wey mah help he'll set himsel up in Glesga. Oh yes indeed, he says tae me, I really must say that you have given me a taste for blue-nosed blood.

Well, that wis enough fur me. A sees mah briefcase lyin next tae mah chair so's A grabs it an two haunded chucks it at im but he jist flaps at it wey the back eh his haun an whoosh, the whole thing jist busts open an aw mah stuff goes flyin everywhere. But, ya beauty, therr right bi mah feets lands mah souvineer fey Wembley thit A cerry wey mi whaurever A goes. It's mah bit eh the goalpost that A gote when we invaded the pitch efter beatin the English oan therr ain turf. Cuz if therr's wan thin A hate mair thin the Tims it's the Guffs. So anywey, A picks up the bit a wid an starts tae sort mahsel oot fur the attack but the Count's staunin therr wey is funny eyes an even though he's no openin is geggy A can hear im saying, You are in my power. You must do what I tell you. An right enough A feel like A'm startin tae go under his control. Then he goes, Ha ha ha. It would have been better for you if you had taken the crucifix from the peasants, an it's that thit does it fur me, A'm beelin an A gets the wid in both hauns wi the pointy bit stickin oot an A jumps up an sticks it right through that Count's hert.

Whit a scene then, A cin tell ye. He sterts thrashin aboot makin a noise like the Celtic support when Raith beat them in the cup final an aw his skin sterts shrinkin, like ye cin see noo that he hus big fangs cuz is lips urr peelin away back fae his mooth an then he jist dries up an crumples tae the flerr an aw thit's left is a pile eh dried skin an his claithes. Oh aye, an a pretty smert ring thit A pocketed fur mah troubles.

So's that's how A became a vampire, an a pain in the erse it is anaw. A mean, fur wan thing, A can noo only go tae see games at night, otherwise A'll git aw frizzled up in the sun. An A've also gote this ungoadly cravin fur bludd. A mean, if A goes tae the pub A cin still take a pint eh beer an that. The trouble noo is that it tastes like pishwater. Mind you, whit's new aboot that? But whit cin A dae? A canae exactly go intae a pub an ask fur a pint eh rhesus negative, cin A noo? They'd think A wis a poof ur sumthin. It's quite good wey the birds though. They aw tell me thit A've gote these sexy, hypnotic eyes, so's A jist sterrs it them like that Count sterred it me an Boab's yur uncle. The trouble is, A never seem tae be able tae get a shag. Like, they'll come back tae mah place awright an the'rr right intae suckin mah face, but before A know whit's happenin A'm suckin therr necks an then the'rr deid. Well they urr noo. At first A didnae know whit A wis daein an A must uv been leavin them a wee bit alive cuz noo A've gote loads eh these brides eh the undeid stoatin aboot aw wantin me tae tell them whit tae dae an askin whit huv A brote fur them tae feed oan.

So's efter A wiz turned intae a vampire an that, oot therr in Transylvania, A decided tae dae a bit eh travellin. A wiznae too sure aboot this at first, like wis therr rules ur sumthin thit A huv tae follow, so's A looks through the Count's library an sure enough he's gote loads eh stuff oan the undeid an A learns that if A wants tae travel aboot A huv tae take wey mi some eh the turf under which A wis buried. Well that wis a bit eh a proablem cuz A wisnae buried. Efter A killed the Count A jist soart eh dozed aff oan the flerr an then wakened up the next night deid an a vampire. But A wis no tae be ootdone bey the rules eh the supernatural. Wan eh the other things A always carry aboot wey me when A'm away fae hame is mah wee bit eh the turf fae Ibrox that A keep an nurture an A found it worked a treat. A lie in mah boax, put the turf oan mah chist an that's me soarted.

So's Ah'll tell ye aboot mah travels in the old countries.

Here, wait a minute. Before A stert, whit time is it? Naw sorry, yi'll hiv tae go. It's time fur the fitbaw oan the telly. Naw don't tell me the scores, A want tae find oot fur mahsel.

A'll tell ye wan mair thing before ye go though. Yon commentator, Gerry McNee. Is he no meant tae be a Celtic supporter? If he is he's gonny get it in the neck wan eh these days.

**Anne Frater**

## RUITH

Siuthad, 'ille, ruith.
'S tha thu glè cheart.
Nam biodh an roghainn agamsa
chan fhuirichinn còmh' riums'
a bharrachd.

## RUN

Go on then, run.
And quite right, too.
If I had the choice
I wouldn't stay with me
either.

## SREANG

An e gun robh sgàile air mo shùilean
nach do mhothaich mi roimhe?
Feumaidh e bhith gun robh.

Chì mi nis an sreang eile
gad tharraing air falbh bhuam
's gun de chomas agam a bhriseadh
fiù 's nam bithinn ag iarraidh.
Tha mo shnàithlean-sa air a ruidhleadh
a' feitheamh ri fear eile.

Tagh thusa do shreang fhèin
ach cha bhi mise
aig ceann seach ceann dheth.

## STRING

Were my eyes clouded
that I didn't notice before?
They must have been.

Now I can see the other string
pulling you away from me,
and I don't have the strength to break it
even if I wanted to.
My thread is reeled in
waiting for someone else.

You choose your string
but I won't be
at either end of it.

Raymond Friel

## MORTAL
### after Gauguin

Jake had spent the bank holiday drinking.
Around tea-time he gubbed a regular
For some innocuous half-cut remark,
And was bundled outside by the owner.
They scuffled on red gravel but the angel,
With nicotine-stained wings and a technique
Perfected from a thousand such brawls
Soon had his neck in an unbreakable lock.
Folk drifting home from the theme park looked on,
Wondering whether or not to be amused.


## STANLEY SPENCER IN PORT GLASGOW

English, war artist, he wandered the braes
With a mind lit up by Lithgow's burners –
Through the charred sandstone of Princes Street
And the wasted spaces of Devol,
Unimpressed women guarding the black mouth
Of a close, kids lobbing 'whistling' stanes
Over the white flags of the washing-lines;
Till he came to the Blitz-fed cemetery.

The eyes wide enough to let in heaven
Were blank to passers-by, the purr of doos,
The automatic fire of riveting.
In time, the mound of wet grass and headstones
Re-emerged in the gloaming; Port Glasgow's
*Resurrection* granted, bar the painting.

Robin Fulton

## ANCIENT STONES VISIT US
(Ales stenar, Skåne)

The colours have lost
their evil opposites today. Ghost-free.
Our grey cells are blue,
dandelion-yellow and willow-green.

Gravity has eased
the pressure of its hands on our shoulders.
Our feet have chosen
earth. They balance our unequal life-spans.

The stones have acquired
the lightness of paper lanterns, an art
of standing unmoved
whatever winds blow. They imitate stones.

In their present tense
the stones have no understanding of age.
We leave the warm field.
We have been here much longer than the stones.

Valerie Gillies

## GIE US MILK
### (from the Gaelic milking song *Thoir am Bainne*)

Ma hinnie sall hae caufs wi white cluifs
an a band tae gae bonnilie roon her haughs
nae bourach o herr nor hather, o lint nor strae
but a tedder o silk brocht frae ower the border
        O ho ower the border!

        Gie us milk, broon coo
        lat doon strin and strone
        gie us milk, broon coo
        wat the bairnies mou!

Ma crommie sall hae girse an fauld
she sall hae hicht an howe an white grun
she sall hae blawgress, windlestrae an stibble
she'll hae a sowf o mountain dew frae the stey braes
        O ho the stey braes!

        Gie us milk, broon coo
        lat doon strin an strone
        gie us milk, broon coo
        wat the bairnies mou!

## COOL CAP

You couldn't have a serious conversation
with anyone who looks like me
under the cool cap during chemotherapy.

A cobalt blue two layered helmet
like a Woman-in-the-Wind biker wears,
the cap comes out of the freezer. Icecrust on it.

When the great wave comes crashing
and the chemicals rush to my scalp
the cap stops my hair falling out.

The freezing layer caps the globe.
I'm under the permafrost, it's preserving
this nomad woman with her six horses.

Here's my needle tattoo on kidskin, my weird
colour hair, my strange crescent headgear.
Let in today's air, I melt away,

fading out the derbyday trampling beat
of those wild gallops on the high plateau,
the grip of this hard hat thawing.

Jules Horne

## QUITE THE THING

My dad says I'll maybe have to do pictures. I've never done that afore but I've seen it on the telly. They've got eyes and faces for everybody in the whole world. That's why I've got to do the man.

You can see our bit gy well from up the hill, seen it's white and fair stands out from the others cos it's painted. You can see the back bedroom window and work out where the slanty attic one is with the no curtains behind the Hoggs' bit. If Jane's coming to our bit I go into the back bedroom so I can see her come out the front door, miles away, this wee walking dot, and I ken it's her, though. That road I ken to get ready. And I kent she was coming, cos we'd phoned about it.

I could do the pictures first, maybe. If you want. While I remember. You could do Dad or Mum even or anybody or maybe me. Have you got bits for me in there? Eyes and that? When did you get them?

Where we were was at the tyre. It's good tyre, up by the cemetery, up the back brae, and you can get a good scary swing. You can birl ana, sideyways, cos it's just the one rope, and you can get somebody to birl you and birl you till the rope's tight, and then you can birl back the way, with the sun getting in your eyes, round and round till you get dizzy and maybe a wee bit sick from screaming. But it's no scary. The best thing is to stand up and put your head back and look up at the tree, but Ali can only sit as she's five.

We found a den in the gorse bushes. You can tell it's a den cos there's sherbet dab tubes on the ground, and matches, but we didna play with matches. You're meant to strike them away from you so you dinna get burnt. I've never seen anybody there but they must come and go cos of the sherbet dab tubes. They must be on their holidays ana.

In the books in the holidays they have ginger beer. It's aye lashings and tastes magic and cold and there's this dog and boats. I dinna think we're allowed it cos it's beer but they're English. My dad has beer locked in a cupboard under the table he made. It's formica and he made it in the shed.

We sometimes get lemonade, but it's dear. Once my cousin came and wanted diluting orange in his lemonade, but my mum goes, either or. That's the Kelso ones.

Jane had a tube of Smarties so we divided them into colours and ate them. She goes, dinna eat them all at once, like my mum, but we did. There was blue ones in the picture but you never get any in the tube.

Anyroad, this man came up the hill. He was bigger than a dot because we could see he had a jaiket ower his shoulder, holding it with his one finger. I canna mind what colour. Maybe brown. I suppose it was kinna funny to be out for a walk cos it wasna Sunday and there was no houses up the hill. But anyroad it was Jane's go so I lifted out Ali and Jane sat in the tyre and cawed and I pushed.

My dad does a thing where he pushes you till it's high enough to run right under the swing and then you go really high. Sometimes I get scared that I'll go right round the top and fall, but my dad says you'd stay put cos of the force, but I dinna believe him. The rope is straight like a kinna stick holding you down and sideways, but when you get to the top it'll fall like wool and that'll be you.

So this man gets nearer. Jane goes, maybe he's got lost? I go, must be gy donnert as all the shops and that are down the hill. He gets up to us and looks fair serious and goes, what's the time? and it's a quarter past three. Then he goes, have you seen a wee white dog, and we go, no, and we think he must have lost it, and then he can't be that bothered cos he goes, do you want a push? Then Jane starts kinna giggling and I look and then I pretend I didna look cos he's got his thing hinging out.

I ken I shouldna have giggled but I couldna help it. He was pushing Jane on the swing and his thing was hinging out and he hadna even noticed. He must have walked all the way up the hill, maybe even along the street and that, quite the thing, and folk looking. I didna fair look though.

When you do the pictures and that, can you do, like, all bits? Like all the bits of the body?

He was gy tall, as tall as my dad, and maybe about the same age. You'd think he'd notice, but then I suppose it's gy easy to forget. You often forget to do your zip and then it's dead embarrassing when you've been to the toilet. No at school, mind, cos we're no allowed trousers at school.

And he was smiling and quite the thing. Ali didna ken what I was giggling for but she was giggling ana. She does that. He pushed Jane really high, and I suppose it was gy scary, but you couldna tell cos she was just hinging on and laughing and cawing and being quite the thing. And maybe we thought we'd get a shot ana, with him pushing.

But this went on for a while with him pushing, and we didna ken what to do except hing about, so in the finish we ran down the hill. Or maybe I ran down the hill and Ali came with me. I didna really leave Jane because she was on the swing and anyroad there was no place else to go so we knew where she was. We ran down to the den and waited. Me and Ali.

We were in the den and we ducked down and I go, did you see that? But Ali didna ken what I was on about and I wasna going to let her go and get a look. Anyroad she's only five.

You canna go on the tyre after it's been raining. Leastways, you can but it's got water in it and leaves and you have to lift it up and cowp it out but you have to be careful or you'll get soaked. I got soaked once. You have to pull up the tyre right up by the bottom and then leave go and then it falls and kicks kinna jaggedly like and the water comes out. It's gy heavy, mind.

So after a bit we're waiting down in the gorse bushes and wondering what to do. We canna get Jane cos she's up on the swing and we canna get her down and anyroad it takes a while for the tyre to stop. Like when you try to jump off at the real swings, you have to wait until it feels right or you'll just do your knees in. Like when you get wee stones and muck all stuck in your hands from falling and it's fair sore. I had a teesh scurl there once.

He had on kinna brown clothes or navy, and trousers and this jaiket on his shoulder. I canna mind what he did with the jaiket when he was pushing. I canna mind the trousers. I didna fair like to look. I was looking at his face cos it was the only place you could look. He had big eyes and they were dark and he was kinna bald and he didn't have wee eyes, no, they were big. Like those cartoon ones you draw with a circle and a line through the middle for the eyelids. Like Deppety Dawg. Aye. Like those. And the hair. Less. More in the middle, like a V. Like that. Dark.

That's great. That's just like.

My grandad's bald. I asked him once how he didna have hair, though he used to look like Clark Gable in the photos, and they all laughed, my mum and dad and everybody. And he goes, an accident. And he goes, something hit my head. They all laughed again and I was fair vexed for him because it isna that funny, something bashing your head and losing all your hair, like a roof and that, like the trapdoor in the attic because I saw that once and it looked fair sore.

It's like, I'm forever growing out of things and my mum is aye at me with the scissors and you'd think folk could grow their hair back, especially as he's a hairdresser. It must have been a gy big accident but they dinna talk about it. We have chips there when we go to Kelso, from the place next door. And we have sandwiches to put them in but she puts on too much butter and you have to bite it with your teeth like cheese.

Ali and me are down in the bushes and we're wondering what to do, but we dinna want to go back up cos he was pushing gy hard. And we dinna stick wir heads up because we're still giggling. But then Jane comes down, quite the thing, and goes, maybe we should get back. I go, is he away then? and she goes, uh-uh, and I

go, was that no scary? cos it was gy high, and she goes, no. She's
older than me.

We wait in the den for a bit and when we look out he's away.
But Jane's fair tane with hersel cos she got a push off him and she
goes, you shouldna have giggled. And we go home.

It's the next day and I'm still giggling at the man who didna
even notice about his thing, so Mum goes simmer doon, I'll give
you something to giggle at. I'm greetin but I canna tell her because
of Jane and her mum who'll kill her, but in the end I do tell her
though I canna remember how cos I dinna say 'thing'. It comes
out about the man and she phones Margaret and then Dad and he
phones the police and Jane's no gonna speak to me cos we'd said
no to tell. Jane's mum Margaret goes, I know nothing about it,
and Jane gets asked and you can tell she's no gonna be my best
friend any more after that.

No, he didna touch us, cos we ran away to the gorse bushes
and you have to ask Jane about the rest. He was tall and thin
with Deppety Dawg eyes with a line through for eyelids. Hair like
a baldy V.

I seen him again after that. He walks by us gy ner every day on
the way to school but he doesna look at us. You'd have to come
with us and I'd show you. There's this new girl came, he's a pal of
her dad's and comes about the house. I told her but she didna
believe me.

You see if you get new people, who're just born, how do you
get their eyes and that? Or maybe you just use the parents' eyes, if
they're the same.

That's the best mouth. I'm no sure if it's his. Maybe somebody
else's. I canna fair mind the mouth. But that's his eyes. Definitely.

Jane got a clouting off her mum. She's still not speaking and
she's got my Action Girl. You say to your mum, dinna tell, and
what's the first thing they do? And she goes, tell me, tell me, if anything like that happens again. And she looks at me fair hard and
goes, now you will, won't you? and I go, yes, with my teeth shut
and looking at her hard ana.

But I dinna ken if I would. You can get into the awfest lot of
trouble.

**John Hudson**

## BRUCKNER'S NINTH

We broke our trip by a wooded stream.
The stand of oaks, old Anton reckoned,
Had leaves that numbered half the sum
Of life left him in twice the seconds.

At the castle gates he seemed quite calm;
His room gave onto groves and lawns.
But then he asked me in alarm
Why stars dissolve within the dawn.

Poor soul. We closed out night, left quill
And ink in hope he might complete
His symphony. We counted on God's will,
Soon heard the marking of a beat,

Watched sheets of paper fall like leaves –
Then read a score of empty bars.
*The notes*, he cried, *that fill these staves
Must number heaven's countless stars!*

Note: *Bruckner suffered a neurotic obsession with counting.*

**James Hughes**

## COMMA

Did you notice me?

In that beautiful line,
that heart stopping phrase?

Did you notice me?
I bet you didn't.

Just a comma, the lowest ranking footsoldier
in punctuation's pecking order.

Smaller than a colon, the dictionary defines me.
A colon: two specks of fly shit on the page
of history.

But me, this tail of mine relates me to my
glamorous cousin.
That flaming longhaired star, the comet.

So when next you hold your breath,
in that blissful hiatus that heightens desire,
think of me.

That pause
comma
between this heartbeat
comma
and the next.

**Robert Hume**

## UNTITLED

Thunkit doon oan the flair
Fae the beuroo flew my Scots Thesaurus, an
Rumplit left the pages fluttrin thair.

First oot fae the wreckage poppit up *perjink*.
Wi barely a care for the scuffilt pages
– his former hame, or so you'd think –
He pufft his shouders up, gave the flair
Sic a look, twas naught but bare disdain;
Then wi sniff and snoot,
The very acme of applied aplomb in all but name,
He dustit himself doon, an set strollin oot
– naethin so common as a scuttlin there.
Perhaps on the hunt the whiles for dalliance
Wi some southron sweetie named Insouciance.
Next, muscularly, came a burly chiel, *disjaskit,*
Puffed, sleeves up, face red an reddnin,
Braces tight but mou slack, cam pokin roon the corner
O a chaptir fur a new task. I pointit towards the gairdin.
He paused only to pluck at the cover o the buik
Then wis oan his way.

Eftir that, business grew brisk
As freens an neebors passit by:
*Dunt* an *wanner* exchangin blows;
*quine* an *lassie* hasting
To be far from *beldame*'s witherin eye;
*Beelin* an *ragin*
Fa'in oot wi *stammygast*;
*Donner* an *gloamin*
Renewin an acquaintance fae the past
*Fozie* an *creashy* an *glaur* slippt slowly by,
More like to flow, more slow than fast, but
Still too quick fur *draigle*, at whose heels,
Wanly, *girn* was aiglin to nip, while a the time
Tryin to keep ayont the hoat breath o
*Hochmagandie* – flushed, poogled,
Labourin, but
Wi a broad, neighbourly smile oan his face
(I wasna sure, but I think I kent him

Once.
Did he live next door,
or had he known ma wife before?).
As ye wid
Expect, eftir thon, things racit by:
*Mixter* an *maxter* trippit each ither up,
*Oxter* disgraced himsel –
I'll no say why
An *tapsalteerie* had tae be towed away at last
Fur – eftir some turns – finally squerrin up tae *stramash*;
*Scunner* seemed tae take a lang,
Lang time tae pass
Then things got quiet – like.
Nae fash
O camp-followers, naeb'dy cam
Tae fill ma anxious pause. But
just as I was set tae streitch my airms towards
The lighter tome, tae haud it just masel,
There came a rustlin, then the book was couped.
Timmed oan its end,
And that by a word I shoud
Have kenned, as well as I ken noo
*Thrawn* bent himsel roon the heap
O rumplit pages, then hunkered doon oan it
– nae comfortable, of course –
Aye lookin the while at me fae neath his broo,
As if tae say *Am no fur movin.*
*Well Am no pickin it up* I thought, but didna speak.
We noddit, each to other, two sons,
Like Love an Hate, o but one mother.
An settled oursels doon
To wait.

George Inglis

## JEAN AND MARY ON A TREE

'Gaunnae geeze it, Jeannie?' he said, 'gaunnae geeze it?' His hauns were aw ower the place. He shoved them up ma skirt, in ma blouse, roon ma back tae try an loosen ma bra; he wis squeezin ma arse, kissin ma neck, he hud his tongue in ma ear; fuck, he widdnae lea me alane.

An did yea gea him it? Did yea let him? asked Mary.

Did ah fuck! Thon wee bandy bastard? Christ he's a wee fuckin greeze ball. Ah wid let auld Jimmy Stevens dae it tae me afore ah'd let him. Noo, if it wis Mister Henderson that wis pleadin wi me, if it wis him that wis rubbin himsel against ma leg and pantin in ma ear, well that wid be different. But wee stinky arse McFall? Nae fuckin chance.

Jeannie and Mary both succumbed to a fit of the giggles. They were sitting near the edge of a wood on the trunk of a fallen tree, swinging their legs to and fro beneath them. Mr Henderson was their English teacher. They both fancied him, had the hots for him. Not a day went past but they talked about him, fantasised about him. But he was ever beyond their reach.

When dae yea think yea will dae it wi somebody, Jeannie? asked Mary.

Jeannie thought for some time over this. Ah don't know, she said, but ah really want tae dae it. Ah'm dyin tae dae it, jist dyin tae. But the thing is, lassies huv tae be cairfu. If yea gae it tae jist anybody, then chances ur they'll go an blab aboot it.

Look whit happened tae Agnes when she gaed it tae Sammy McTavish. Christ dis he no go tellin everybody whit a rear wee shag she is. An Agnes cannae say she never done it can she? An noo aw the boys want tae shag her, thinkin she'll be easy.

Mary looked thoughtful. Aye, yer right enough, ah suppose. Wid yea dae it wae yer brother, Jeannie? she said, quite the thing.

Ach, ah've thought aboot it, but ah don't think sa. Ma cousin Sadie said she done it wi her brother a couple a times. She says maist o them dae it in the Gorbals. Bit it disna seem right tae me. Whit aboot you?

Naw, ah widnae dae it wi mine. He widnae dae it wi me anyway, likely. Ah think he's a poof.

A poof?

Aye. Ah think he is. Well, ah'm sure he is.

Jeannie laughed. Christ almighty. Your brother a poof! Ah canny believe that. Ma sister's goat the hots fur him tae. Aw she talks aboot is your bloody brother. It's Johnny this an Johnny that. Ha, ha. Wait tae ah tell her that!

Whit makes yea think he's a poof anyway?

Ach. Ah jist dae. He's no interested in any lassies at aw. He spends aw his time wi Davy McDonald. They disappear fur oors thegither. They're ay whisperin tae wan another, an laughin aboot daft things, an ave seen them lookin at other boys the way some lassies dae.

Ach, that disnae mean they're poofs. Ah'll tell yea aboot poofs. Ah wance saw ma uncle Bobby wi a man. It wis at ma granny's hoose. Ah went there wan day tae see her, but there wis naebody in. Ma granny ay lees the door aff the latch, so ah went in.

Ah wis sittin in the kitchen jist pettin the cat, when ah heard this noise fae upstairs. It wis like a groanin noise. I thought maybe ma granny wis in, that she wis upstairs no well in her bed or somethin. But when ah went into the lobby, her coat an hat werny there where they usually ur.

So, ah went upstairs. The noise goat louder an louder, it came fae the back room. The door wis open a wee bit, an ah looked in. An there wis ma uncle Bobby an another man in the corner o the room. Ma uncle Bobby wis bendin ower wi his arse in the air. The other man hud his troosers at his ankles an he wis rubbin ma uncle Bobby's arse. Christ ah near died. Ah stood an watched for a while. The other man called ma uncle Bobby his 'good wee boy'.

Then ah ran doon the stairs an oot the front door. Ah couldnae look at ma uncle Bobby fur weeks efter that.

They both laughed. Christ almighty, said Mary. Ah never thought yer uncle Bobby wis like that. Is he no a leader in the Boys Brigade or somethin?

Naw, the Scouts, said Jeannie. He must prefer boys in kilts.

They laughed wildly at that. Boys in kilts, said Mary. Ha, ha, ha.

Ah wish ah had seen somebody daein it, said Mary, even if it wis only a couple a poofs. Ah've heard ma mother an faither at it, but that's aw. An ah've seen ma faither's willy when he's been drunk, an ma brother's when he wis wee, but that's aw.

Who wid yea really like tae dae it wi, asked Jeannie. Apart fae Mr Henderson that is. Ah mean, *really* like tae dae it wi?

Ach that's easy. Ma next door neighbour, Andy Smith.

Whit, Alfie's faither?

Aye. Ah think he's dead sexy. Ah watch him fae the back room windae when he's oot in the gairden cuttin the grass. Ah get aw wet jist watchin him. Then ah staun there an rub masel till ah come.

Well, Mary, I never! A nice girl like you doing a naughty, dirty thing like that. What *would* your mother say? said Jeannie in her poshest accent.

She probably does the same, laughed Mary. Ah've seen her watchin him tae.

Mary laughed loudly and flung her arms around Jeannie's neck.
O Andy, I do love you so. How would you like to shag me?

They both fell off the tree laughing, tumbling down amongst
the long grass. They lay laughing uncontrollably for some minutes,
then wiped their tear-filled eyes.

The sun beat down on them. It was getting warmer.

As they lay side by side, the birds twittered around them and
the sounds of insects filled the air. Tufts of dandelion cotton float-
ing on the light breeze.

Christ, said Jeannie, it's warm. She sat up and pulled her jumper
over her head, her long hair falling over her face.

Mary sat up and pulled hers off too. Her hair was shorter than
Jeannie's. She always admired Jeannie's hair and wished hers was
the same – long and blond and shining in the sun. Mary's hair was
thick and wiry. Whenever she tried to grow it long it just seemed
to get thicker and thicker and ended up like a 'frizz bomb' as her
mother said.

Jeannie put her hands on her forehead and caught her hair,
flicking it back over her head and smoothing it down gently.

Mary sat up and tidied it from the back. Running her fingers
through it and spreading it over Jeannie's shoulders.

Jeannie could feel herself becoming damp. A bead of sweat
formed between her breasts. My goad, she said, it's warm the day.

Aye, said Mary. Roastin. She let her head fall back, exposing
her neck to the full glare of the sun. Her breasts swelled out, pushing a gap in her blouse.

Jeannie did the same. Her breasts were not as well formed as
Mary's. But she tried to compensate by arching her back more and
thrusting them out a little further.

Mary sat up. It must be the warmest day o the summer so far,
eh? Ah'm bloody swelterin. She undid the top two buttons of her
blouse. Ah wish we hud oor swimmin costumes oan. Then we
could get a bit o a tan.

Jeannie sat forward too, brushing against Mary's arm. We've
goat oor bras on, huven't we? We could jist take aff wir blouses.
There's naebody here tae see us.

Aye, said Mary, so we could.

Fuck it, said Jeannie. Ah'm takin ma bra aff tae. There's naebody here but us. In fact, ah'm takin aff ma skirt tae.

Aye, fuck it, said Mary. Why no?

They giggled as they took off their blouses. Da da da da, da da
da da, laughed Jeannie as she held up her bra and twirled it around
before letting it slip to the ground.

Mary laughed and joined in. Da da da da, da da da da, they
both said as they took off their skirts.

They looked at each other and laughed nervously. Jeannie

looked at Mary's breasts. They were huge compared to hers, and her nipples were large and dark brown. Jeannie's breasts were smaller and her nipples were pinker and tiny compared to Mary's.

Christ Mary, look at the size o your tits. Ah wish ah had a pair like yours.

Aye, ma mother says that tae. She says she disnae know where ah get them fae cause it's no fae her.

Mary put one hand under each breast and lifting them up walked over to Jeannie. A pair o bazookas, ma mother says. Bam, bam, bam.

She bumped her breasts against Jeannie who faking being shot, slumped to the ground and lay with her eyes closed.

Mary sat down beside her. Your tits are no that bad, she said. In fact, there's nuthin wrang wi them at aw.

Jeannie opened her eyes. Ach, they're too wee.

They're no too wee. An they're firmer than mine, look. Mary held one of her breasts out to Jeannie. That's the trouble wi big tits. They get aw droopy.

Jeannie sat up. Aye, she said, looking down at her small, firm breasts. Ah suppose that's wan thing. She ran her hand over her breasts, then fingered her erect nipples.

Aye, said Mary. Ah'm getting that way tae.

Jeannie looked at Mary's large, dark nipples. They stood out firm and hard.

Christ Mary, she said, yea could hang a jacket oan they nipples o yours.

Mary burst out laughing. So yea could, ha, ha, ha.

Jeannie jumped up and grabbed her blouse. She fingered at the tab until she had teased it out from the blouse, then placed it gently over the nipple of Mary's right breast. It hung for a moment then slipped off as Mary shook with laughter.

They flung themselves back down on the grass, writhing in uncontrollable laughter.

Slowly the laughter subsided and they lay still, side by side.

Each could feel the warm dampness of the other's sweat as their arms lay against one another's. They said nothing.

The light breeze got suddenly colder and a large cloud blotted out the sun's rays. Small drops of rain landed on the girls, forming clear beads on their breasts and arms.

Quick, said Mary. It's goanny pour.

They both jumped up and grabbed madly at their clothes, fumbling at their bras and staggering around as they slipped their feet into their skirts.

That's ma blouse, ya daft galloot, said Mary laughing, as she watched Jeannie struggle with the buttons.

Christ, so it is.

The rain was falling heavy now as they started running down the field.

Ah hope tae fuck it disnae thunder, said Mary.

An ah hope tae fuck there isnae a bull in this field, said Jeannie.

**Helen Lamb**

## SPRING SPELL
From *Thirteen Spells*

The window is my clear eye

New leaf on the willow
Old Glory in its hole

Bed's stripped, mattress turned

New leaf on the linden
Clean sheet on the line

A thorough wind, a scrubbing down

New leaf on the laburnum
Fresh bristles on the broom

Table's waxed, crystal sings

New leaf on the rowan
Old Glory in the bin


## TWISTED MUSE

She comes
when I've all but given up.

She says –
waiting is part of the pleasure.

Have you suffered enough?
Are you hungry and lean?
Do you want me as much as the man
who held you at arms-length
whilst serving his mean
ration of love?
He was clever that one.

Am I better than him?

And now that I'm here
am I worth it?

**Maurice Lindsay**

## THE KIBBLE PALACE

Holding my Uncle's hand, in the Kibble Palace
we left coat-buttoned coldness sealed outside,
as if it were some kind of fatal malice
that statues, plants and goldfish can't abide.

The marble statues fixed unlikely poses,
caught blind-eyed in some ancient secret act
beyond what any six-year-old supposes;
topped high above the ferny bric-a-braque

that islanded the pond where goldfish darted,
trees hung bananas underneath the roof;
glimpsed oranges and lemons, too, half-parted
their sheltered leafy branches, offering proof

fruit didn't grow in boxes. Left and right,
past KEEP SHUT signs, hothouses reached out arms,
and I was dazzled by the scent and sight
of coloured orchids kissing open charms.

Outside again where, meanwhile, Winter mouldered
the footprints of besmirching snow, the real
world moved about its dailyness, hunchshouldered,
chilled by what flowers and statues never feel.

Peter McCarey

# SAPRISTI!

## Sapristi! Mistah Kurtz, I presume[1]

[1]The first word is a mild imprecation, a corruption of 'sacristi'; the second, though it could be read as mimicry of standard southern English, is meant to mark the accent as coming from beyond the pale. The name Kurtz (German for 'short') reinforces the salient feature of the narrative. Imprecation, address, deduction: line by line the story goes back in time, and across the equator from west to east, against the course of the sun.

'I presume' refers to the meeting of Stanley and Livingstone in 1871 on the shore of Lake Tanganyika. Livingstone, wandering like a river, was so low on supplies that he would soon have had to borrow from the very slave traders whose activity justified his presence. He was on the wrong side of the watershed, bogged at the source of the Congo, not the Nile. Stanley had been sent by James Gordon Bennett, editor of the *New York Herald*, to get a story. Though no one in Britain knew where Livingstone was, the consul at Zanzibar knew how to reach him, so the scoop was something of a sham (most of this information is to be found in *David Livingstone and the Victorian Encounter with Africa*, ed. J.M. MacKenzie (London, 1996)). It did bolster Stanley's name, though, and started him on a career that took him down the Congo for King Leopold of Belgium, baptising the font with much African blood. Joseph Conrad's *Heart of Darkness*, published in 1901, recalls a journey he himself had made on the Congo in 1890. The bloody Kurtz and the calculating manager of the ivory business are two sides of Stanley. They meet not at the source of the river, but well downstream, at Stanley Falls. The phrase 'Mistah Kurtz' is pronounced on a boat returning to what must have been Leopoldville, now Kinshasa. The boat is next seen heading up the Mekong with Martin Sheen on board, looking to terminate Marlon Brando with extreme prejudice. So far, so good. Sapristi, though the word does occur in Agatha Christie (perhaps as a private joke: the blood of Christie), is much more common in Hergé. *Death on the Nile* doesn't fit: this is *Tintin au Congo* (alternative translation: Nothing Doing on the Congo), where Tintin, a foreign correspondent, like Stanley, and indeed like Michael Herr who wrote the screenplay of *Apocalypse Now* (see above), is there for a story. Tintin is Belgian, though he doesn't boast about it. As a journalist he hits the Dark Continent well after the missionaries and just ahead of the diamond smugglers. He declines big money from American, British and Portuguese agencies – he may be in cahoots with the French – and takes over a country that looks like a Kenyan game park, not a Congolese forest, peopled with Robertson's Gollies. His methods are those of Prospero and Mistah Kurtz. Like them he can be defeated by no one but himself. He's a loose cannon that gets airlifted out to his next assignment before Conrad's cycles of desire, temptation and surrender can so much as skew his quiff.

Where are the women? All I recall in Tintin is an exceptionally glaikit-looking mamma on a train; not a speaking part. The comic is the land of the grunt (see Michael Herr again, his book *Dispatches* on the Vietnam War). The mysterious stranger is geography, even in the other Rambo, *'je est un autre'* (the other one-liner of 1871). Mistah Kurtz? It's the same for him. There only are two women: his intended back in Brussels and the African queen – again not a speaking part, more a figurehead. The narrator says, 'Girl! What? Did I mention a girl? Oh, she is out of it – completely. They – the women I mean – are out of it – should be out of it. We must help them to stay in that beautiful world of their own, lest ours gets worse.'

I presume the moral is clear: Livingstone was living in a cartoon strip. A funny hat instead of a Tintin quiff, but similar tuppence-coloured pictures of him being attacked by a lion, and folksy photos of his attendants in pantomime African dress. Meanwhile Livingstone's wife, too often pregnant, explored the rooming houses of London. Hers should have been a non-speaking role too, but she joined him on his penultimate trip, and she drank and she drank and she told him she didn't believe any more in any of the religion he had been pushing in Africa, then she died on him.

That appeared to be that: another piece of fiction explained away, an open-and-shut case, till what did I see on the front page on 4 December 1996? 'Terrorist Bomb on Paris Train Kills 2.' Yes, yes, that too, but this: *'International Herald Tribune* – Frozen Water Found on the Moon'.

'Pentagon scientists, speaking at a news conference, said that radar soundings by the Clementine, an unmanned spacecraft, had confirmed the existence of a large mass of ice in an area of permanent shadow near the lunar south pole.

'The southern crater, known as the South Pole-Aitken basin, is 12 kilometres (more than 7 miles) deep, which makes it the deepest yet discovered in the solar system. The lake is estimated to be tens of feet deep.'

*The Times*, 4 December 1996: '... Material at the bottom of a crater nearly 8 miles deep is frozen water. The guess is that the water was carried there by a comet which crashed into the moon

3.6 billion years ago, creating the South Pole-Aitken crater ... The ice lake is estimated to be 25 feet deep and 200 yards wide.'

The source is an article in *Science* (Vol. 247, 29 November 1996, 1495–8). It begins: 'The possibility of ice on the moon was suggested in 1961.' In fact, it was suggested seven years earlier in *On a marché sur la lune* (Hergé, *Les aventures de Tintin*, Paris/Tournai, 1954), where Tintin and Captain Haddock find some in a cave.

But earlier in that book Tintin as he leaves the rocket describes '... a nightmare landscape, a landscape of death, of terrifying desolation ... Not a single tree or flower or blade of grass ...' Dante likens the scene to the River Adige as it passes through Trento, though he saw not a comet but Satan crashed into the middle of it, for geographically the Inferno looks like nothing so much as this crater on the moon with a frozen pond at the bottom. In Dante, though, the moon is a nebula, outermost suburb of Paradise.

But why am I telling you all this? And which of you is Mistah Kurtz? Is Conrad's heart of darkness on the Congo or on the Thames? T.S. Eliot thought he knew when he wrote 'The Hollow Men': 'We are the hollow men ... Headpieces filled with straw ...'

'It seemed to me that if I tried I could poke my forefinger through him, and would find nothing inside but a little loose dirt, maybe.' That was Conrad's narrator on an employee of the ivory export company. Of the company manager, Conrad's narrator says, 'It seemed to me I had never breathed an atmosphere so vile, and I turned mentally to Kurtz for relief – positively for relief ... it was something to have at least a choice of nightmares.' Eliot, I guess, was afraid of being like them; his fear was proof he wasn't. (Later, when he found the Church, he lost that fear.) When Tintin did London (*The Wasteland*, Faber & Faber, 1922), the ace reporter dedicated his text to Captain Haddock *'il miglior fabbro'*, thus likening the dedicatee to Arnault Daniel and himself to Dante. Quite a double act. There they were up country, like Romans in darkest Britain at the start of Conrad's story. It's nice to get on with the natives, but if that's too much trouble, you make a wasteland and you call it peace. You know, shantih, shantih, shantih, the peace that passeth understanding unless you read the footnotes.

'It was morning and Belacqua was stuck in the first of the canti in the moon. He was so bogged that he could move neither backward nor forward. Blissful Beatrice was there, Dante also, and she explained the spots on the moon to him. She showed him in the first place where he was at fault, then she put on her own explanation. She had it from God, therefore he could rely on its being accurate in every particular. All he had to do was to follow her step by step. Part one, the refutation, was plain sailing. She made her point clearly, she said what she had to say without fuss or loss of time. But part two, the demonstration, was so dense that Belacqua could not make head or tail of it. The disproof, the reproof, that was patent. But then came the proof, a rapid short-hand of the real facts. A bistatic radar experiment measured the magnitude and polarisation of the radar echo versus bistatic angle B, for selected lunar areas. Observations of the lunar south pole yield a same-sense polarisation enhancement around B=0. Analysis shows that the observed enhancement is localized to the permanently shadowed regions of the lunar south pole. Radar observations of periodically solar-illuminated lunar surfaces, including the north pole, yielded no such enhancement. A probable explanation for these differences is the presence of low-loss volume scatterers, such as water ice, in the permanently shadowed region at the south pole. Belacqua was bogged indeed. Bored also, impatient to get on to Piccarda. Still he pored over the enigma, he would not concede himself conquered, he would understand at least the meanings of the words, the order in which they were spoken and the nature of the satisfaction that they conferred on the misinformed poet, so that when they were ended he was refreshed and could raise his heavy head, intending to return thanks and make formal retraction of his old opinion.'

I've spiked that first paragraph of Beckett's 'Dante and the Lobster' with the abstract of the *Science* article mentioned above, trusting you can distinguish God from the Pentagon. Piccarda? Piccarda, most beautiful of women, more beautiful than ever. Your father put you in a convent, your suitor removed you. The vows you were obliged to make you were compelled to break. That lost you your place in the front stalls of heaven, though you are happy there in the pale outer reaches as you were in the convent, as you were at home. But the spots on the moon are gab-broid basalt, the rest is granite. You can't float there like sunlight in a raindrop. Mary Livingstone, ugly as an aardvark, uglier still when a miscarriage partly paralysed your face. Your father had given you to a fellow-missionary, who sent you home to squalor. That lost you your faith and drove you to drink. A decadent and a heretic. You're not even a poet. Miranda, there are not so many stories in the end; this is a tale of misappropriation. Nothing I can tell you will prepare you for the day. *Heart of Darkness* is only *The Tempest* told by an upstart duke, who arrives just as his brother's act is finally coming apart (the magic does get very rough at times). There's a beautiful Ariel poem where Eliot at first can do no wrong:

'What seas what shores what grey rocks and what islands
What water lapping at the bow
And scent of pine and the woodthrush singing through the fog
What images return
O my daughter.'

then he lapses into another bloody sermon.

I give the floor to Sebastian Barker and the *Long Poem Group Newsletter* (No. 2, February 1996): 'When, after a period of seven years' composition (1935–1942), Eliot finally managed, in the face of the Blitz, to complete *Four Quartets*, he made what Lyndall Gordon in *Eliot's New Life* (OUP, 1988) called his "Nijinsky leap": "Poised over the turning rim of the wheel (of time), he now made for the hub, the still point (of timelessness)." In making this leap (an inescapable act of courage if the poem were to cohere as a whole), it appears he felt obliged to make a conscious, irrevocable, public commitment to mystical Christianity, albeit tempered and make steadfast by the Presocratic philosophy of Heraclitus. In Eliot's case, it is this core of indubitable sincere belief which helps to hold the disparate parts of the poem together. The successful reception of the poem gives us a transparency of a good part of western consciousness at the time, that is to say in the jaws of totalitarian terror. Further horrors were to come to Eliot's mind: the death camps, the atomic bomb. What kind of Nijinsky leap, we might wonder, must be attempted, following Eliot's example, to reconcile human pain and divine love now?'

Holy smoke.

There's a painting by Henry Raeburn on the cover of Tom Scott's *Penguin Book of Scottish Verse*, the one my generation grew up with: The Reverend Robert Walker skating on Duddingston Loch. (If you can't see the picture, read the poem by David Kinloch.) Arms folded, one leg stretched out behind him, he has just completed the pirouette that drew the painter's attention to him. That minister has eyes you could skate across. Duddingston Loch is a mirror of oil and canvas. He slices the freeze-dried faces of Dante's traitors bedunk kaschlikk, splitting them like kail and cauliflower. Recongeal. It says the Rev. Robert Walker. But I'm not sure.

Sapristi!
Mistah Kurtz.

Derrick McClure

## TWA SANGS
### frae the DAIN DO EIMHIR o Sorley MacLean.
### Owerset frae the Gaelic bi Derrick McClure

## IV

Oh lass wi the yella, lourd-yella, gowd-yella hair,
your mou's muisic an Europe's mane,
oh lass sae bonnie, lichtsome, lockerin, fair
your kiss wad wile the wershness frae thir days' shame.

Wad your sang an your bonnieheid's glory tak awa
the deid fousome uggin o thir ongauns,
thaim at the heid o Europe, the reiver an rochian,
an the auld sang singin in your mou reid-vauntie?

Wad your white bouk an brou's sun tak frae me
yon blaik bedritten traitorie,
the attery creed an spite o the bourgeoisie,
an the merghlessness o our Scotland sae dwaiblie?

Wad bonnieheid an lown muisic twyne
the frushness frae me o this cause ayebidin,
the spang agin skaith o a Spanish miner,
an his great saul gaun doun but pynin?

Whit war the kiss o your lips sae pauchtie
aside ilka drap o praicious bluid faa'n
on the gowstie fells cauld an frostit
o the bens o Spain frae a steel column?

Whit ilka link o your heid gowd-yella
tae aa the puirtith, dule an hert-rug
faa'n an tae faa on the fowk o Europe
frae the Ship o Slaves tae the haill fowk's thirldom?

## XIX

I gied ye immortality –
tae me, whit wes 't ye gied?
Nocht ava but the stangin
flanes o your bonnieheid.
Ye gied a gurly onding
an the stoun o mony a pynin,
wormit tae my spreit
an glory's skaithfu shinin.

Gin I gied ye immortality
ye gied it back tae me:
ye pit a gleg edge tae my spreit,
tae my sang, a glister free.
an houbeid 't wes you that connach't
my bounheid for the faucht,
gin I coud see ye e'er again,
mair, an the haill, I'd claucht.

Gin I coud see forenent me –
forgotten aa my pyne –
on Tir nan Og's green lawlands
your loesome form sae fine,
I wad hae naethin ither,
tho my stang ye'd bring yince mair,
an the lown my spreit hed wan til
again war skaithit sair.

Oh bonnie, lint-haired lassie,
ye rave awa my maucht,
ye snorl't the gait I traivel't,
tho my ettlin o't wes straucht;
but gin my steid I'se win til,
the wuidit heichs o sang,
ye'll fire my lilt, an shap me
tae a Makar wi the stang.

Houbeid this stane I heistit
on time's unsiccar bens,
it wull staun there for a moniment
aye or the warld enns.
An tho anither taks ye
an ye ken na o my dule,
my sang sall be your glory
whan your fairheid's cryn't tae muil.

**Euan McCulloch**

## SUGAR AND SALT

As I sat in the cafe
I watched the boy
at the next table
carefully taste his coffee
to see
whether he had added
white sugar or salt
from the paper sachet.
I could not tell
what was in his mind
but agreed that the taste
of sugar or salt
was something
you should take the time
to check
and I laughed
sitting with my own cup
of filter blend
as I thought of chance
          sugar
             and salt.

Murchadh Dòmhnallach

## AIR AN ALLABAN

Eilean air acair san loch
Nach buannaich cala a chaoidh
'S mi fhìn air bhog
Sa bhaile mhòr chèin
Nach buin dhomh
Nach tuig mi.


Murdo MacDonald

## EXILED

Island
Anchored in the loch
Finds no harbour
And I afloat
Bobbing
In the bright lights
Of bacchanalia
My aliens
Who cannot fathom
Me.

82

Anither teeny wee playlet by Janina MacDonald

## WEEMIN'S PROEBLEMS

### CHARACTERS
Auntie Aggy • Pheemie Hen • Jimmy's Jeannie
Tarbrush • The Laddie • Narrator

| | |
|---|---|
| Sound Effects | Soft waves ir jist lappin oan the shore. A herring gull sits oan a chumlie an says, 'Gub, gub, gub. Gub, gub, gub. Gub, gub,' rhythmically, jist like the morse code. A Scottish traditional tune cums oan the radio (The Hen's Maerch tae the Midden), tae the beat o scrubbin flairs, an beatin mats, an wringin oot wet flair cloots. |

*Enter Narrator, Auntie Aggy an Pheemie Hen.*

| | |
|---|---|
| Narrator | Auntie Aggy an Pheemie Hen ir jist sittin doon oan thir auld bench ootside the tarred washhoos wi a wee cup o tea. They'd been reddin oot thir hooses a moarnin, scrubbin flairs, shakin oot mats, scrubbin an pittin swirly paetterns oan thir doorsteps an noo it wis elevenziz. A ritual of ordered cleanliness. Aye, cleanliness iz next tae Godliness an aa that, followed by a wee sit ootside in the sun. |
| Auntie Aggy | Aye, Pheemie Hen, it's a no bad day the day. |
| Pheemie Hen | It's swelterin. Ye dinnae git mony days like this. |
| Auntie Aggy | Aye. That's an awffie bonny blooz yer wearin, Pheemie Hen. |
| Pheemie Hen | Och, A jist dug it oot the back o the wardrobe the ither day. |
| Auntie Aggy | Dinnae lean back, hen, the tar's meltin. Ye'll git yer blooz a manky. Ye ken, the collar's awffie neat an the brooch gawns real nice, hen. |
| Pheemie Hen | Wiz ma granny's, Auntie Aggy. |
| Narrator | An Pheemie Hen pattid er shooders in pride. They sighed a sigh an sippt thir tea an took a wee chomp oot o thir rich tea buscuits. |
| Sound Effects | The Tarbrush polka, wi heavy seabits ploddin doon the brae tae the herbur. |

*Enter Tarbrush an the Laddie (in the distance)*

| | |
|---|---|
| Tarbrush | Right then. |
| The Laddie | Aye, Tarbrush. |
| Tarbrush | Ye goat the kindlin? |
| The Laddie | Aye. |
| Tarbrush | The matches? |
| The Laddie | Aaaaye. |
| Tarbrush | Right, laddie. Let's git oan wi it. |

*Exit Tarbrush an the Laddie an fade music etc.*

| | |
|---|---|
| Auntie Aggy | Thir doon the herbur bilin up the tar again. |
| Pheemie Hen | Aw naw. They pick thir days dint they. Oan a bilin het day. |
| Auntie Aggy | They'd tar awthin geen half the chance. It's no easy tryin tae keep awthin spankin clean whin they cum up wi a wee pot o tar, no wantin tae waste it. |
| Pheemie Hen | 'Twunty pund tae pent the kirk? Tar the bugger,' e says, whin they run oot o white pent. |
| Auntie Aggy | Whit? Whae wis that? |
| Pheemie Hen | Tarbrush. Ye mind, whin they run oot o pent fur the kirk. |
| Auntie Aggy | Tuh! A might i kent. |
| Pheemie Hen | Whitever thir pentin, ye kin bank oan thim gittin aw ower the heid wi the stuff an awthin else forebye. |
| | Och hear cums Jimmy's Jeannie, pair lassie. |

*Enter Jimmy's Jeannie*

| | |
|---|---|
| Narrator | She'd three bairns wi er. Yin oan er airm, anither tryin tae hing oantae er leggins an no mikin much heidwye, an the third yin wis oan reins an tryin tae git away tae where she's jist cum frae an squishin er juice. |

| | |
|---|---|
| Jimmy's Jeannie | Tuh. Aw. Jist hoo dae ye dae it? Ye've slaistert Ribena aa doon yer Telly Tubby teashirt. |
| Auntie Aggy | Hoo ye daein, hen? |
| Jimmy's Jeannie | Nithin much, Auntie Aggy. Jist daein away. |
| Auntie Aggy | Yer lookin fair trauchult, hen. |
| Jimmy's Jeannie | Well ye ken whit it's like. A'm fair exaustit wi thae bairns. Ah've been up a nicht wi the wee yin. |

| | |
|---|---|
| **Pheemie Hen** | It'll no be lang afore they gawn tae the skill an ye'll git sum peace. The wee yins goat a fine pair i lungs oan im, hen. |
| **Jimmy's Jeannie** | Aye. |
| | (An she thocht), 'Peace! Peace! That's easy fur them tae say. Ony maun thit looks it that pair wud need thir heid seen tae.' |
| | A'll see ye. |
| **Pheemie Hen an Auntie Aggy** | Aye, hen. |

*Exit Jimmy's Jeannie*

| | |
|---|---|
| **Auntie Aggy** | She's an awffie corperation oan er, though. |
| **Pheemie Hen** | She's ... thon wye ... again. |
| **Auntie Aggy** | Naw. |
| **Pheemie Hen** | AAAAAAye. |
| **Auntie Aggy** | Er maun diznae hing aboot, diz e? |
| **Pheemie Hen** | Mind she aye fa's easy. |
| **Auntie Aggy** | That's fur share. |
| **Pheemie Hen** | A'm affie sorry fur the wunch. She's aye rinnin oot tae the lavvy, heavin an bockin an that. Er mither cum doon tae look efter the bairns the ither day an she went doon tae Hyemooth wi her sample, ye ken. She didnae hiv yin i yon plastic thingmies so she din it in a wee boettle o Spar Blend. Er maun aye likes the Spar Blend. Woodnae thank ye fur a malt fur iz Christmas. An she didnae like tae pit the wee boettle in er shopper wi er purse, so she laid it oan the flair unner er seat oan the bus. Well! It wisnae there whin she goat tae Hyemooth. The laddies ahint er hid snaffelt it. |
| **Auntie Aggy** | Mercy. That ud pit them aff the whusky fur life. |
| **Pheemie Hen** | Guye wearsht. |
| **Auntie Aggy** | Serves em right! |
| **Pheemie Hen** | An that's no the hauf o it. She phoned up fur the result an goat tellt she'd goat a urine infection, an tae pick up er Auntie Biotics as sin is poesible. The lassie wiz fair flumoxt. |
| **Auntie Aggy** | Ye dinnae say. |
| **Pheemie Hen** | Aye. |
| **Auntie Aggy** | Typical! Ye'd think wi a tha computerization an that they'd it least git it right. Pair lassie. |
| **Pheemie Hen** | Onywye, it wis Jimmy's mither, granny Jeannie thit goat tellt bi the lassie oan the phone, |

'Congratulations, Mrs W., your result is positive.'
An granny Jeannie says, 'Whit dae ye mean yer
positive, hen?' An the receptionist lassie says,
'Congratulations, Mrs W., you're expectin.'
'Whit did ye say, hen? Expectin whit?' she says.
Well ye shood i seen the state o er. Whit a caerrie
oan. The wumin wis fair aside erssel. Ye ken!
She'd been watchin ower mony Kilroys an
Vanessa's aboot the matuere weemin thit hae
bairns it fifty an that.

**Auntie Aggy**      Bit er maun's been deid for ower ten years.

**Pheemie Hen**      That disnae stoep ye worryin aboot it! A mean,
onythin's poesible. A mean, ye dinnae even hiv tae
hiv ... SEX ... thae days. Yin skoosh an yer away.
Invitro-insemin-wadjimmy-ca-it wi sumbuddy in
a mask an a white coat.

**Auntie Aggy**      Cum oan, hen, that's fur coos.

**Pheemie Hen**      It's fur folk anaw noo.

**Auntie Aggy**      Never! They didnae hae that in my day. Wud a
saved bilin hunners o white sheets an a that
postin an manglin blankits ...

**Pheemie Hen**      Will ye no listin, wumin! An ye jist need tae sit
in the WRANG PLISS an that's it. In the CLUB.

**Auntie Aggy**      Sharely no, hen. Ye dinnae believe that dae ye?

**Pheemie Hen**      NAW. Bit A'm beginnin tae wunder. It's catchin,
ye ken.

**Sound Effects**    A slow air (Sunset Achnacloich) wafts from the
distance with waves lappin oan the shore.

**Narrator**         They baith sippt thir tea an stared intae space jist
rhueminatin oan sumthin. The sun wis jist beatin
doon an the tar wis seepin oot an rinnin doon
the washhoos wa. Uncommon quiet it wis. It wis
guye warm. An they shiftid an fidgitied oan the
bench an felt the het wud through thir thick
tweed skirts.

**Sound Effects**    Fade out music, etc.

*Enter Tarbrush an the Laddie (in the distance)*

**Tarbrush**         Shovel mair coals oan, laddie. Stoke er up. The
tar's so near bilin.

**The Laddie**       Smithereens! That's hoo oo'll end up ye daft
bugger.

| | |
|---|---|
| **Tarbrush** | Kin ye no tik a bliddy tellin. Stoke er up. Mair coals, an A'll hae nae mair o yer bluddy impudence. |
| **Narrator** | An Tarbrush gees the Laddie a right smackeroo oan the chops. |
| **The Laddie** | Ooya, ooya, ooya bugger ooya. |
| **Auntie Aggy** | If ye dinnae mind, hen, A think A'll feenish ma tea in the hoos. A feel like sittin oan ma AIN chair. A'm wiltin, an the heat's makin iz fair flustert. Ye cummin? |
| **Pheemie Hen** | Nuh. Ye dinnae git it this het that offen. |
| **Auntie Aggy** | A think ye shood cum intae the hoos, hen. |
| **Pheemie Hen** | Naw. A'm enjoyin massel. |
| **Auntie Aggy** | Yev no been merrit, hen, ye dinnae ken … |
| **Pheemie Hen** | Look am fine. |
| **Auntie Aggy** | Ye dinnae ken whae wis sittin ther this moernin. Him, HIM, doonbye. Cum oan, hen. |
| **Pheemie Hen** | Nuh. A'm enjoyin massell. Ye dinnae git mony days like this. |
| **Auntie Aggy** | Oh hen, ye dinnae ken. |
| **Tarbrush** | The tar's bilin up fine. Pile oan mair coals, laddie. An geed a gude shovelfae this time. |
| **The Laddie** | Ye'll hae us a blawn tae buggery. A'm gittin the hell oot o'd. |
| **Tarbrush** | Ye'll bide here an stoke er up. Mair bluddy coals! |
| **Narrator** | An the laddie pits oan a few mair coals. E wis feart, an guye chairrie aboot the hale thing. |
| **Tarbrush** | Laddie, yer yissless. Gees a hud o the bluddy shovel an A'll did ma bluddy sell! Erse fur elbi, wi aathin, that's whit ye ir. A'll show ye hoo it's din. |
| **Pheemie Hen** | A think A'll sit an sook up aa that sun, Auntie Aggy. A'm fair enjoyin massel. |
| **Auntie Aggy** | Ah well, soot yersel. |

### Exit Auntie Aggy

| | |
|---|---|
| **Narrator** | Pheemie Hen tiltid er heid back, exposin her neck an chins in a thir glory, unclasped the brooch, an undid the collar button o er bonny blooz. An er knees relaxed momentarily an partid. |

Pheemie Hen wis AWAY. It wis a blisterin het day. An the tar wis rinnin doon in globbules.

**Sound Effects** The sea lapping oan the shore, an then a muckle big wave crashin, a awffie whoosh, like a lum gawin ahud, the glob glob glob soonds o the biling tar and then a muckle blast an reboond i orgasmic proportions, fallaed b a couple o seconds silence, then gulls squawking hysterically. 'Cawl, cawl, cawl ...'

**The Laddie** Bluuddy hell!
**Tarbrush** See, A telt ye it wiz bilin up fine.

**Sound Effects** A few wee tunes – 'The Tarbrush Polka', 'Whit Happent' (a slow air), an anithr yin, 'The Moernin Efter Peels' (a jig).

James McGonigal and Hamish Whyte

**virtual memories**

**from MIND**

Anne had her picture taken
holding her great long-haired Orkney cat
Flaccus (after Quintus Horatius
– a long way, he was more genie than genial).
She stared at the camera, daring you
not to worship this wild, yellow-eyed god
of 39 Clouston Street, Kelvinbridge.

\*

Talking of hair, that blond poetic lad
out of Glasgow Academy or Hutchie Grammar
(all the same) whom we called Sappho
came up to us in University Avenue
all aquiver with literary excitement:
'Are you going to Philip's on Sunday?
Tom's going to read his poem with "fuck" in it!'

\*

Saturday afternoon playing drums
with the jazz band, Clarkston
Rugby Club Fete at Overlee Park
(I was supposed to be in Portpatrick
seeing Ishbel but didn't go
so had to share the kit with the sub):
good crowd and Dunks was there
taking moody snaps –
after tea with Gordon to see
*Psycho* at the Classic, Renfield Street:
when we got to the bit with the swinging light
and the mummy's mummy
the audience went hysterical
and this girl on my left
grabbed my arm
and screamed 'Mammy! Mammy!
– oh yes, a full social life
at fourteen.

\*

My mother said
when she was expecting me
she was ill for months
with 'pernicious pregnancy'
kept throwing up
went down to five stone
and Doctor Cameron threatened her
with termination
if she didn't put on more weight.

\*

Henry falling headfirst into the silt
at Kingholm Quay. Then the ride home,
mud on the backseat leather. The shadow
of his scarecrow shape etched on Solway mud.
Rbt Burns Exciseman walked that harbour rim.
Nith's current pulsing out or beaten
back by the tide: washing the mudbank smooth.

\*

When we got engaged her father
made me a miniature ladder
(adjustable to twice its length),
a hint, I think, at elopement –
saving him the embarrassment
of morning coat, speech and ceremony
and possibly money.

\*

Aunt Margaret at the vd clinic
talking to her patients harshly
and sisterly. Learned that from her father
cobbling on the kitchen floor who let fly
with a tackety pit boot as she crept in
late and just deliberately
missed.

\*

My brother Graeme and I
loved that part of the cheese
nearest the rind –
so savoury-sweet –
when the cheddar was almost gone
we would grab the end-bits
from the table and run
into the front room and hide
in the corner beside the piano
under the standard lamp
and pretend to be mice
nibbling food snatched from the trap
g-naw, g-naw.

\*

greyer, I note I'm becoming
anecdote and memory
on my children's lips,
not cruelly but sometimes
wrong in the detail
surely

\*

My first death: probably
my grandmother's: very young
I took it comfortably enough
sitting on the kitchen stool
staring through the open door –
we had blackcurrants and raspberries then
in the back garden. She was part
of my summer holidays for a while,
taught us card games in the sun lounge
when it rained, like strip jack naked,
and I beat her at draughts, unaware
of the child's privilege of allowing
his elders to win. When we came home
from Arran there were rasps to be picked
if birds or neighbours hadn't got at them
first. I went with my father to see her
in hospital: a damp night, we changed
trams, I sat at the foot of the bed
reading space comics while they talked.

\*

Drove to the Campsies in the wee Fiat,
parked in the dark. Unable to express
myself I lifted her, carried her to the
threshold of the scarp: all Kelvin's dale
below us, orange streetlights marking out
the roads we'd come by and the road we'd go.

\*

home from town in the crowded train
uncorrected proofs of
Adrian Henri sandwiched between
a Littlewoods Crusty loaf and 8 tomatoes
(two split)
Kenneth has new shoes
(and a painting-box)
Winifred has new shoes
(and sore feet)
I have two Oxfam books
(the other one O. Henry's *Rolling Stones*) –
coming out of Pollokshields West station
Kenneth points up to the blue 5 o'clock sky
and shouts 'Look, a whole moon!'

\*

The smell of bacon and babies
intermingled forever. That morning
my father at the corner of the stairs
said: 'You've got a new brother'
Probably his fifth son. Myself talking
to my own children about my father,
awkwardly.

\*

Read *Sir Gawain and the Green Knight*
and started my own alliterative epic
about King Arthur's white knight
with the help of Chambers Twentieth Century
Dictionary in the back bedroom
I shared with my brother
sitting at the converted dressing table
in the glow of light from a Lewis's desklamp –
where I heard the Beatles' first broadcast
doing my homework (Paul being left-handed

could stand nearer to John at the mike)
and Sylvia Plath's last:
she said 'daddy, you bastard, I'm through'
in a voice that spoke in my head
ever after.

*

That I should have reached the age
when to touch the nape of her neck
each morning is more important
to me than it is to her, probably. Don't
know. Don't care.

*

My mother said once she was starving
to death in a room in Edinburgh, sick,
distant from her family. Some Catholic
neighbours sent for a priest, who made sure
she was fed, and survived. That's why
she became a convert. Seemed to lose faith
when my father died and she survived.

*

Claire with the legs of Ginger
her cat friend dragging along the carpet
as she held him, hauled him
into her world of feline language.
He accepted all that.

*

the gleaming brass ashtray
on the mantelpiece
made by Grandpa
from a German shell casing
hand-polished in the weary hours
aboard the minesweeper

*

repainting the flat for one daughter returning
from Praha – a bed reconstructed in the recess,
pine wardrobe, hoping she'll fit like the furniture

I remember lifting the cot back down
through the loft hatch, repainting it white
in the light from the middle window

lifting her clear of its bars when she cried

\*

in that stuffy bedsit in Chapel Lane
she pinned my poems on the wall
along with the postcard Picasso
and Beardsley
listened to home-made tapes
of the Incredible String Band
(waiting for my cough between two
of the tracks) –
she wrote:
'your bottle of cider sits alone half-full
my lips remain unkissed for 3 whole weeks'
while I was off in Greece –
and so
too often uncertain of each other
at any great distance
we lapsed

\*

Two Christmas pedal cars, blue and red.
Mine smaller and less chromey than
my elder brother's. More like a tank.
I'm pedalling hard.

\*

A noticeable dampness in the house
whenever we returned from a journey:
musty, mousey, what we had no
time for, getting into bed to sleep

and rise again. Ignore what's surfacing.
There's work to be done. Once a weasel
ran in from the garden and down the cellar.
My father closing the door behind him

carefully as he descended.

\*

In Niddrie Road a wee Pakistani girl
wearing a child's sari stopped me
smiled and asked 'Who are you?'
I said 'I don't know, do you?'
but she just smiled again
and walked away.

\*

Bev and I wore our CND badges:
rebels at the Young Liberals' garden fete
helping Roy with the bookstall
discovering the real pleasures
of 'helping with the bookstall':
the rummage for your own treasures –
from a box under the table
came into my hand *The Lady in the Lake*
1954 reprint old green and white Penguin
photo of the author on the back
a vaguely academic type with pipe
holding a black furry two-eyed mass –
was it the mocking-Scott title
or the 'Mystery and Crime' the cover promised?
whatever, my diet of Doyle, Christie, Marsh,
James and Stoker was now spiced:
city-centred, simile-crammed, smart-witted,
sleazy, cynical, sentimental, stylish
a new world said read me.

Rob Mackenzie

## DO YOU REMEMBER HENRY HEALEY'S?

Don't preach the virtues of Peckhams
to me, your fond impression of
its delicatessen, your strange obsession
with peppered salami.

No, give me an honest grocer,
greasy sausage rolls and cut-price
custard creams and I will remember
Henry Healey's,

and you, the new romantic, high on
quiche cocaine, grinding your crotch
against the kitchen door, shouting,
*Fuck this party*

to the black-shirted indie crowd,
tortilla dips on their lips and
creamed prawn vol-au-vents
staining their goatees.

These were the eighties, the long days
you came to stay, cooking beef
curries in the non-stick wok
we thought exotic.

Now we revise dietary history
in the drive-thru Burger King,
queue with the motorway set,
trying to forget.

## JUDAS AND THE CANDLE

I'm not ready to burn
with you, candle, I'm no Messiah
groping in the darkness for a Lucky Strike
to set my hair on fire.

You're glaring from the altar
at tongues of love and perfumed necks and boys
in white dresses; without irony you light up
the sins of the flesh.

The longer you burn, the lesser
you become, candle. I've borne enough
scalding tears without catching yours,
waxed around your ankles.

I squint through the stained glass;
an old man, a bitter, arthritic fist
on a stick, the squall nailing him to a tree.
I blow hard. It is night.

Donal McLaughlin

## SURVIVING UNCERTAIN FATES

At some point I started: jumped awake; my hands darting into the
dish on the tray in front of me; the tips of my fingers landing full-
square on chicken-skin I hadn't eaten. Drew, when I looked, was
still across the aisle. Beyond the exits next to our seats snored folk
who'd been to the same island, among them the father of five
who'd hung, drunk, over the bannister, toddler on his shoulders
and all, as a slow queue, well past its sleep, worked its way down
to the plane. The memory of everyone side-stepping the duty-free
dribble from that guy's bag, and I dozed off again.

Some time later came the chime: seat-belts for landing, doors
to manual, etc. We both woke this time, turned, and looked at
each other. I wasn't with it – said so, myself. Drew nodded,
grinned, said, 'Great impersonation of Tommy Cooper earlier, by
the way!'

'So you saw that, did ye?'

Chuffed with his ammo for future slaggings, he grinned again.

'Bastard! Never miss a trick, do ye?'

He was on for a carry-on, launched into a Cooper impersonation just as I did. The meal trays had been removed in the
meantime.

We landed. The worst winter this century, police saying not to set
out unless you have to. We had to. Drew driving, the long trip
north from the airport, in the highest gear possible, crawling, con-
centrating. Ahead of us the likelihood of burst pipes, flats in a pure
mess when we got there.

'Just like that!' he quoted again, out of the blue, and laughed. I
laughed, too, able to take it, as he ooh-yugh-ed and wiped his fingers clean. Just summit else he'd witnessed, shared, I thought. His
laugh, though, faded: eyes now studied me, were watching for
reactions.

'Can I tell you something?' he asked.

I hesitated before I nodded, I suppose.

'There's something I should tell you,' he told me.

He took me back to Boxing Day night on Fuerteventura. The
shellfish soup, the paella outside the restaurant. I minded fine.
Minded, too, the girl who was singing; her sidekick on keyboards,
his medley of Eurovision entries.

It was Drew's turn to nod, and I could see he reckoned it safe
to continue.

'Well, mate, that night, I woke up, desperate for a slash, and

when I came back: the way you were lying – shoulda seen it!'
   He paused, maybe testing the water.
   'Out wi' it, ya bastard!' I laughed, like there was nothing I
couldn't handle. 'What was it about me, then?'
   'Not so much you as the pillow,' he said.
   'Pillow?' I asked. Bugger was enjoying this.
   'Well, it wasn't so much *across* your bed, as *down* it!'
   'Aw naw!' I groaned. 'So I'd been shagging the pillow and
you, ya bastard, saw the evidence. Ya jammy –!'
   That was the reaction he wanted, of course: revenge for the
time he was paralytic in Stirling and I claimed he'd snogged Susie
Fraser.
   I was damned if I was saying another word. I wouldn't give
him the satis-bloody-faction. He reached across, but, and sort of
shook my shoulder. 'It's not what you're thinking,' he said.
   'Both hands on the wheel, you!' I barked, shrugging him off.
'Specially in these conditions.'
   'But it's nuthin embarrassing, mate,' he protested. 'It's *good*.
Speaks for you. That's why I wanted to tell you –'
   'Right, that's it! Stop the fuckin car!' I said. 'This'd better be
swift'n'painless – for *your* sake. Pull in at a convenient place and
effin out with it, mate!'
   'And don't forget your hazards!' I added as he came to a halt.
Way I was feeling, he'd be needing them.

What he told me was brilliant.
   Seems I was facing the wall, and my sheet was well down the
bed, practically off me. Thing he focused on but was the pillow,
parallel to my back behind me: where Claire had been until six
months ago, where she'd been since second-year uni.
   'So that's what this is about? Us separating?'
   'Shoosh,' he said.
   It seems my left arm was out from under me and over and
round the pillow. 'Round *her*,' as Drew said. 'Round Claire,' he
added as I looked at him, no' believing I was hearing this. Ye go on
holiday wi' the bugger, ten days over Christmas and New Year, and
on the last leg of the journey home he starts playing the amateur
fuckin psychologist?
   'So six months later, I'm still not over it, still missing her. Is that
what you're saying?' I asked. 'Me hugging the pillow contradicts
everything I told you down by the pool, confided as we hiked
across hardened lava. Is that the story? I don't still love her, if that's
what you're suggesting.'
   'Naw, that's not what I'm saying, mate. It's more than that.
What I'm saying is: at that moment, I saw you, and I saw the
pillow, and I saw what she walked out on. I saw the love you're

capable of giving – and I'm no' goney see that otherwise, am I?' he added hurriedly. Must've seen I wasn't sure how to take this. 'All I'm saying, mate, is: what I saw underlined what I've told you before: you're some guy –'

He reached across and patted my shoulder again; looked me in the eye.

'*Her* loss,' he said.

You'd forgive me for thinking that that was that: that the heavy bit was over, and I could now relax. While he was at it but, he decided to tell me that it was as if I slept in slow motion. I looked at him again: the fuck was he on about now?

The explanation could've been worse: before he dropped off again himself, he'd seen me turn in my sleep. Seems I did so fraction by fraction, millimetre by millimetre. As if someone had been sitting opposite me with the video remote-control, pressing the still-frame and slow buttons. 'Aye, like *you*, ya pervy bastard!' I tried to protest; there was no stopping him but. At one point, he said, he thought I would reach a brink, then topple over or collapse. Even then, but, it seems, I rolled in controlled fashion onto my back.

Seeing me, he'd ended up wondering whether he slept in slow motion, too? Did everybody? Funny how he'd never noticed before with Sandra or Ann or Marie, he said. Or with Clare, *his* Clare, he hastened to add, Clare-without-an-I, or Valerie or Sam, for that matter. He'd got onto Naomi, Pamela and Sharon before he couldn't keep a straight face any more. I hit him a thump. 'Braggin' proddy cunt!' I said.

'Least I've got summit to brag about!' he'd answer, I thought. What he actually said was: 'Maybe you've got to be on the other side of the room from someone, sometimes, to see what's going on.'

What *really* tickled the bugger but was: before he conked out again himself, he'd spotted that my right hand had a hold of the last corner of the sheet, and always, always, no matter what way I turned, made sure my privates were covered. The distance between the sheet and my stomach remained *constant*, he maintained; the *precision* was incredible.

'So there ye go: virginity well oot the windae – still the bashful Tim, but!' he teased.

'Least I wisni playin wi' myself like you'd've been,' I joked. 'Naw, that's the magnetic pull of the Catholic belly-button! Makes sure we stay *dacent*. You Prods haveni got that!'

There was a pause. Him (unusually) not rising to the bait. Me realising *that*, and *why*, my hold of the sheet had been perfected while I was still under my mother and father's roof. Minding being lucky as fuck the morning my da came in (he never did) to say John Paul I was dead. Sometimes things crop up that make you see you're not as free as you think – Claire and her convent-girl night-shirt came to mind'n'all; Claire who made out she was being *subjected to eyefuls* if ever I slept naked beside her. Claire who accepted nudity only in the bathroom or when *doing it*. If she wasn't up for it, she didn't want to have *that bloody thing* staring her in the face, she said.

Drew broke the silence, could sense something was wrong.

'Did I do right to tell you, mate?' he asked. 'Bout the pillow and that?'

'Aye, mate. Cheers. Ye did right.'

I was lucky he'd seen me. Lucky he'd decided to tell me. I'd tell him another time about Claire; nuthin he doesn't know, anyway. Would have to give him a laugh'n'all: tell him about JP1 dying – and me starkers and hardly under the bloody duvet.

Right now but, I wanted to savour what he'd told me. *The love you're capable of giving.* Was the same boy said I always *pull sooner than I surrender* (that's the Catholic in me, too, he claims). And when I was doing my *hurt-hedgehog impersonations* (as he called them) after losing Claire, was him coaxed me into opening up again; who insisted that *having nobody is not nothing.*

I'd been quiet for too long. Was his turn to feel nervous.

'Did I, mate?' he pressed. 'Are ye sure? Did I do right to tell ye?'

I looked at him. 'Aye, mate, nay worries, ye did right. Ta.'

I waited until I saw him relax, then hit him wi', 'Last fuckin time I share a room wi' you but, ya poof!'

He laughed. We shook on it. A clumsy attempt at giving each other five. He studied my face, grinned, made to get into gear; interrupted himself but to look at me again and give me a hug.

'Cheers, mate,' I muttered as I eased out of it.

He checked his blind spot and we set off again.

Anne MacLeod

## JOHNNY HURT SAYS

when the cows are sitting down
like those cows over there
it's going to rain

look at them, field after field of them
crumpling the longer grass
like brides in adverts in ivory silk
their great eyes softening
to the veil

the mist of creamed cow-parsley
waiting like them, waiting
round the edge of the field
all along the uncut hedgerow

and there's giant hogweed too
not giant yet – erupting –
the still grass and still cows
waiting for the rain

in their dry place

a strategy that never
holds

**Aonghas MacNeacail**

**cùnntas**

tha mi nise
uile
anns na leabhraichean

chan eil rathad eile
air fhàgail
a-mach
chun a' ghàrraidh

**reckoning**

i am now
wholly
in the books

there's no other road
remaining
out
into the garden

## am beul na coille

seasamh am beul na coille
shaoilte gun robh i gun bhoillsgean,
a duibhre ag ithe nam priobadh,
nan aiteal, nan leus

cò chunnacas a leithid
de bhoillsgeadh duibhre

cò chuala a leithid
de dh' osnadh sàmhchair

## in the mouth of the forest

standing in the mouth of the forest
you'd think it was without centre,
its darkness consuming each glimmer,
each glitter, each flame

who has seen such
a radiant darkness

who has heard such
silent sighing

Kevin MacNeil

## the minch

the minch
swallows
the ego's footprints


## autumn moon

autumn moon
bungeeing about the porthole
i'll see you again

Iain S. Mac a' Phearsain

## biadh na h-oidhche

biadh na maidne
ann am beul na h-oidhche
dealbh dhìot
's an teine guail
a' lasadh
's a' spadadh
faileas na doilleireachd
's an astair nach gabh tomhas
le guth
taobh thall a' fòn.

John Scott MacPherson

## nightfood

breakfast
at dusk
your photo
and the coal fire
lighting
and dispensing with
the shadow of darkness
and distance immeasurable
by a voice
on the other end of the line.

## ugh càisge

nam shìneadh leisg
air an t-samhradh seo
nach robh againn thall
's an saoghal ùr gam ghreimeachadh
's na craobhan gam fhàgail freanasach
mu gheallaidhean na seann dùthcha

gabhaidh na rionnagan sgrìob
timcheall a' Chruinn Mhòir
a-null ga h-ionnsaigh
air iomall a' Chuain Siar

's bheir iad asam smuaintean boga
mar phlaosg a rùisgear
bho ugh càisge
's a ghabhar slàn
mus teich am blàths.

## easter egg

stretched out luxuriating
this summer
that Scotland missed
and the new world manhandling me
the trees bewildering me
jumpy about Old Country promises

the stars will take a spin
around the big dipper
over her way
on the north atlantic rim

and they'll strip me of soft thoughts
like an eggshell peeled
from an easter egg
eaten whole
before the heat escapes.

## innis tìle bhochd

cha bu chòir Innis Tìle a bhith ann
's ge b' e cò dha a bhuineas i
chan ann dha nàbaidhean fhèin
a thàinig à tìr-mòr
seach à grunnd na mara balbh

air èirigh bho leabaidh-cuainn
cha chuir i ach clisgeadh air a' chòrr
a dhùisg à brùchd na talmhainn

an truaghan
aig iomall na h-oidhche
fuar is tioram
fo chuibhrig nan rionnagan
nach b' eòlach a seanmhair.

## poor iceland

iceland shouldn't exist
and no matter her pedigree
it's got nothing to do with her own neighbours
from the mainland
as opposed to the dumb sea floor

having risen from her sea-bed
she'll only shock the rest
who woke from a continental belch

the poor dear
at the edge of night
cold and dry
under a duvet of stars
alien to her race.

### ceann Loch an Dala

nuair a tha mi fhìn nam sheasamh
aig ceann Loch an Dala
's mi a' coimhead thar cuain geur
a' deàrrsadh 's a' deàlradh
fo ghrian na sìorraidheachd
chan fhaic mi sgath dhen ghlasadh cheilteach
a' ciaradh Ile
na eilean shìthichean faoin
ach soitheach mo shinnsearan
a' triall dhan iar
Gilleasbaig is Eòghann
a' cur cùl ri Cill' Nèimh
an aghaidh leis a' ghaoith
's an làmhan air a' chliathaich
blàth 's cha mhòr air chrith.

### head of Loch Indaal

personally, when I stand
at the head of Loch Indaal
and look out
over a razor-sharp sea
shining and radiating
under an everlasting sun
I see none of the celtic twilight
reducing Islay
to an island of vacant faeries
but my ancestors' ship
heading for the west
Archibald and Hugh
turning backs on Kilnave
facing downwind
their hands on the gunwhales
warm and almost shaking.

John Maley

# PAPA AND MAMA

Everybody loved Papa Spenser. He was a fine figure of a man. But he was a fool, drinking too much, chasing chickens and throwing his money around. He had silver hair, cut short and neat, and a warm, weathered face. Some guys swore they could see all the colours of the ocean in his deep blue eyes. He always seemed to wear the right thing. When he wore a suit it hung on him beautifully, elegantly. When he dressed casually he looked like he'd just stepped off a yacht somewhere, cool and collected. Some older guys thought they could knock twenty years off their age by wearing Lycra shorts, living half their lives on a sunbed, chewing gum and pretending they could dance. Not Spenser. He seemed to have come to terms with the ageing process effortlessly. A weakness of Spenser's, however, was the demon drink. He wasn't the only steamer in Delilah's by any stretch of the imagination. But somebody as dignified as Spenser had further to fall from grace.

He was an estate agent. A senior partner in a prestigious Edinburgh firm. People said he preferred the Glasgow scene because he found it less pretentious. He was certainly rarely out of Delilah's. He'd often come in alone but for a period of around a year he had been coming in with a lady friend. She was maybe late thirties and called herself Miranda. Nobody liked Miranda. She was rude, bossy and worst of all, used to get pissed and sit on Papa Spenser's lap – a coveted spot if ever there was one. She wore so much gold it would have taken a mining expedition to rob her. There were various tales about Miranda. One of them was that she was a Glasgow madam who built up her business from a spooky bedsit shop to a string of penthouse flats where the good and the great got their rocks off. Other people said she was legit – and had her own accountancy firm. Her presence on the arm of the stunning Spenser was resented by many Delilah's regulars. Guys who had formerly fluttered around Papa Spenser now felt intimidated. Any conversation was now three-way, Miranda constantly butting in. Even when she was quiet, which was a rarity, her gaze was ruthless. No one escaped her scrutiny. Prior to the addition of Miranda to his company, Spenser had always been approachable. He still was, but it was hard to flutter about and fawn over the sweet silver-haired Papa Spenser when everything had to be done under the rather large and snooty nose of Miranda.

'If he'd only get shot of that big-beaked fag hag,' complained one of Spenser's unrequited loves, 'I might stand a chance. I mean who is she? His mentally defective sister?'

'I think she's a scary big dyke,' said a love rival. It was generally agreed that this wasn't the case – that Miranda was straight and that there was maybe a business connection between her and Spenser. Bobbie, a punky lesbian in her late thirties, fancied Miranda. She even claimed to have finger-fucked her in the ladies loo. But as Bobbie had also claimed to have enjoyed similar carnal delights with, amongst others, Jodie Foster and Madonna, her conquest of Miranda was consigned to the realms of pussy pulp fiction. Although Miranda gave the initial appearance of vivacity, it had soon become apparent to anybody with an ounce of sense that she had all the social skills of a rabid dog. One of her nasty habits was to slap whoever she was talking to and guffaw loudly. This was almost forgivable if you had just told her a hilarious joke, but she did it no matter what you said to her. You could have told Miranda your only child had just croaked and she'd skelp you one and howl with laughter. One evening she made the mistake of hitting Joanie.

It had been an especially rowdy night in Delilah's. There had been a karaoke competition with a major prize. A week's holiday for two in Gran Canaria and, swore the compere, all the cock you could possibly suck. The place was mobbed and the sense of hysteria pervasive. In the thick of it were Miranda and Spenser. Every now and then Miranda would unfurl herself from the Papa and go on her rounds, slapping and howling all the way. In the process she knocked a pint tumbler off the bar. Joanie stepped round with a brush and dustpan to sweep up the debris. The problem was Miranda. It didn't dawn on her to either move or attempt to assist Joanie. She simply stood amongst the remains of the pint glass giggling. Joanie grew irritated with her.

'Move yer ass tae I clean up the glass!' he yelled.

Miranda fixed Joanie with a look of astonishment, slapped him hard across the face, and howled with laughter. Joanie wasn't taking this lying down. He slapped Miranda back and in a matter of seconds the catfight to end all catfights broke out. It began in the main bar with a wrestling match that looked like two blind drunks trying to do a waltz and ended in the ladies loo with Miranda trying to flush Joanie's head down the toilet.

Now I'll tell you why Spenser came to be known as Papa. Spenser had a young boyfriend for a while, a young Italian waiter who looked sixteen but claimed to be thirty-one. He had brown eyes the size of small planets and hair darker than the night. He affected a thick Italian accent but it transpired he was born in Govan and had never been to Italy, land of his parents. It was he who christened Spenser 'Papa'. He'd look lovingly at Spenser, drape his arms over his shoulders and sigh, 'Papa.' It caught on and soon everybody was calling Spenser 'Papa'. Even when the

Italian boy had cut loose (a police inspector had offered him a plum position as a houseboy) the name Papa had stuck. Papa Spenser was nowhere to be seen during the Krystle versus Alexis catfight in Delilah's. Bobbie said that he was in the men's room giving a rent boy a wank but her story was never confirmed. Despite his lack of direct involvement in the slapstick fight between his lady friend and Joanie, the management barred both Papa Spenser and Miranda. For a while nothing was seen of him. There was a rumour that he'd sold his business and moved to London and opened his own bar. Bobbie said that she had it on good authority that he had married Miranda and was regularly giving it to her up the arse. Quashing both these rumours, Papa Spenser had come into Delilah's one night with a new lady friend. He presented a small bouquet of flowers to Joanie by way of apology. Visibly moved, Joanie said that as the catfight really had fuck all to do with Papa Spenser, he wasn't banned after all. The lady's name was Edith, she was fifty years old and didn't care who knew. Everybody took to Edith right away. Bobbie, who had initially commented acidly, 'Papa's got a brand new fag hag,' soon ensconced herself into Edith's company, saying she felt Edith had a 'matronly glamour'. Edith tolerated Bobbie.

Edith was a neurosurgeon at the Southern General. Everybody was impressed. Bobbie said she bet she had a good bedside manner and it was only a matter of time before she dragged out another tired old finger-fucking fantasy. Edith didn't know much about her predecessor, but the whole of Delilah's soon dished the dirt. Edith warmed to Joanie and often stood chatting to him at the bar, leaving the coast clear for Papa Spenser's many admirers to put their various proposals to him. One night Edith and Joanie spoke about the catfight. Joanie explained that he was deeply ashamed that he had stooped to violence that night, which was something he absolutely abhorred. But 'that woman', as he called Miranda, had been provocative in the extreme. Joanie also divulged to Edith that his daddy used to beat him when he was a boy and he had vowed never to let anyone hit him that way again. Edith said she had heard Joanie had given a good account of him-self in the barroom brawl. But Joanie shook his head and said his face was nearly down the bend of the lavatory pan and his whole life had flashed before him when Miranda pushed the flush button for the third time.

Joanie and Edith became good friends and Joanie was glad something good had come out of the catfight. He even gave Edith her pet name. As she was Spenser's new sidekick there was only one thing to call Edith. Mama.

**Andy Manders**

## THE EMOTION NOT FELT

here's what I said:
*there are angels in the Raploch too*

what I meant was
I don't go there in the dark

wittering on
about alchemy, injustice and guilt,

impersonating waterfalls
till someone minutes it.

I've been aw they places
wi only the buses for colour

in one wearisome, semi-professional capacity
after another

and aw I fear is death
aw I see is struggle

like rainbows filmed in black and white;
what I feel is something else.

*THERE ARE ANGELS DROWNING IN THE RAPLOCH TOO*

for want of wings and water.
aw they do is shout for bread

aw they get is bread
aw it takes is bread.

aw I have is poems.

aw it is is struggle
wi the emotion not felt.

**Joseph Mills**

## THE BIG GAME

*We're in bed. The Real Coal fire is glowing Disney red orange and
yellow. It's the warmest, cosiest Disney fire ever. And it's a big bed.
Huge. Edward Scissorhands bed: all encompassing, secure. Silk
sheets. Loads of pillows. Outside it's snowing a blizzard. You can
hear the snowy city sounds: the workers hurrying home exhilar-
ated at their discomfort, change of routine, the snow-muffled cars.
You can see the city sights from the wall-long window we had
installed just for that purpose (we're rich): the headlights and neon
glowing through the snow. We've just got perfectly mellow on
Champagne, Malibu and Cointreau, luxuriated in the decadence
of Rum Truffles.*

*I turn to Mel.*

Ryan mimes turning on his left side, resting head on left hand,
makes as though stroking chest of bed companion, and says,
    *'So you finally told your wife then – about us.'*
    Ryan pantomimes framing Mel's jaw with his hand, rolling
thumb over lips, ruffling hair, moves hand down imaginary body,
cradles imaginary genitals.
    *'Aren't you glad it's all out in the open. At last. If only* she
*could have taken it better.'*
    *Mel looks up at the sky. Venus seems to be shining more
brightly through the snow clouds than it's ever shone before.*
    *'Ryan. Darling,' Mel says, staring at the Venusian glow. 'Why
worry about the moon when we have the stars.'*
    *The rough Australian accent still thrilled.*
    *'Angel,' he said. 'You're the only star I want.'*
    'Oh God, I'm going to be sick,' said Brian. 'I mean Mel
Gibson – surely his day is long gone – I mean ten years ago OK
but all that long hair and macho crap now. What's romantic
about that?'
    'This is Mel as Tim, the mentally deficient boy with the big
innocent trusting smile, remember?'
    'And Venus isn't a star. It's a planet.'
    Ryan was going to bitch back – 'God you're such a *Virgo*' –
but Brian suddenly stood up and applauded Gary, one of his team-
mates who had just scored a goal. He ran onto the pitch, kissed
and hugged Gary, patted his bum, hard, ruffled his hair, hoisted
him onto his shoulders so that his muddy-shorted genitals rubbed
against the back of his neck. As he returned from the pitch to the
injury bench he gave the thumbs-up sign to Gary's wife who he'd

spotted in the crowd. Then winced when his smashed knee began
to bleed.

Ryan was fiddling with the bandage over his eye.

'Well you haven't done any better so far,' he said, indignantly.

'OK. *We're in the park,*' said Brian, dabbing at his knee. *'The
sun is splitting the trees. Brad Davis – the Querelle, no the
Midnight Express Brad – is oiling Gary's back. His oiling takes
him further down Gary's body until it's something else they're
doing. Antonio from Sunset Beach is playing football with
Tadzio's boy friend from Death In Venice – no, that Irish guy
from Tomorrow's World. He sees me watching, makes a fist in the
air and slowly unpeels five fingers.'*

There was a huge roar from the crowd.

'OK,' sighed Ryan. 'You win.'

Donald S. Murray

## MOTHER RUSSIA

I can see these islands mirror Russia;
the machair's sweep reflect the steppes
while moors multiply tenfold,
transformed into tundra,
with houses squat in Arctic winds
that shake the fragile edges
of both tree and man.

And the people, too,
clinging to the orthodoxies of Kirk or State
or singing songs sonorous with sadness –
the Volga boatmen crossing seas
to Mingulay;
some cailleach's coat
covering Kruschev or Cherenkov's wife;
Yeltsin reeling through the Kremlin
or the council chamber's doors.

And I am always aware
while recording this dissident voice
and preparing my samizdats,
of how my freedom's circumscribed
by a neighbour's knowing look,
the silence of those citizens
who can send
old friends and fellow-comrades
into internal exile
with a sudden shift of gaze.

Jan Natanson

## LETTERS FROM SCOTLAND

SCOTLAND SCOTLAND It's a small country and shrinking
rapidly.
SCOLAND – Because, you'll have had your T.
SCOLAND (pronounced scowl-land)
LAD – somebody pinched your scon, eh? –
LAD Old Lads: new Lads – invented North of the Border
when England only had Yooffs.
AD – Because John Knox put the fear of L in us
AD That's what you're left with – a soft focus sunlit glen
where kilted Highlanders dance jigs over crossed whisky
bottles, to the beat of a haggis thumped rhythmically
on the lid of a shortbread tin.
DESPERATION is another word
Muddle up the letters and you find
a rope ends it.

Uilleam Nèill

## FREAGAIRT DO LLYWARCH HEN

Nam bhodach liath a-nis
a' streap gu mullach a' bhràighe,
chan eil mi a' còrdadh riut, a Llywarch,
mun bhata càm is riatanach gach là.
Bha mi ro-dheiseil le cainnt, gu dearbh
aig amannan a' feannadh amadan
ro-thric le smùid orm san taigh-òsd'.
Chan eil a' chlann-nighean a' toirt sùil orm
ach cò gheibh cron dhaibh, na luaidhean
is mise mar fheòil righinn an seiche liurcach.
Co-dhiù tha mi nis saor bho na geimhlean
is mo cheangal don chuthaich sin.
Ach tha am bata uinnsinn a' fàs
na charaid dìleas dhomhsa
fhad 's a chuireas mi grèim
air a cheann càm is làidir
a chumas taic rium gu càirdeil
le bhachall dìreach daingeann
a mhaireas, is dòcha, nas fhaide na mi fhìn.
Is tha mi taingeil gur troimh a thoil fhiodha
chì mi a-rithist, theagamh
earrach uaine is samhradh,
foghar òir is donn,
mus tig mo gheamhradh dorcha deireannach.

118

**William Neill**

## ANSWER TO LLYWARCH HEN*

A grey old man now
climbing to the braehead
I don't agree with you, Llywarch
about the necessary walking stick each day
I was too ready with my tongue at times, it's true,
for the flaying of fools
often with a drink taken in the inn.
The girls no longer cast an eye on me
but who would blame them, the dears
and me like tough meat in a wrinkled hide.
At any rate I am free from those gyves
and no longer chained to that madness
but the ash-stick has become
a faithful friend to me
as long as I keep hold of his strong bent head
that supports me in a friendly fashion with a straight, strong stave
that will doubtless last longer than myself.
And I am thankful that by his wooden wish
I may see again, perhaps,
green spring and summer
gold and russet autumn
before my last dark winter comes.

* early Welsh poet who complained about his advancing age
  and dependence on his walking stick.

Stuart A. Paterson

## ROBERT BURNS

Robert burns in the fires of hell
scrawls roaring rhymes with a fiery quill

flytes aeons with Fergusson and Keats
on plateaux of table and bedrock sheets

each hot lick of line burst into flame
from the unholy poets' melting pens.

Upstairs, Jean flings the tea in the bin,
locks the door, goes to bed on her own again.

Meanwhile, smoke clears to reveal the sight
of good rockin down at the old kirk tonight,

Big Daddy Burns and His Smokin Witches
on fire from the apron strings to the britches.

Tom Pow

## ELEGY FOR THE FROG POET
*i.m. Norman MacCaig*

When you said that was it –
your last word on frogs
and positively too –

that was it for us all. So
when I met a frog one night,
idling at the lights, metallic,

sharp-edged on a wet pavement,
my thoughts turned only
to salvation. Besides

I'd little idea just what
a slippery subject a frog
could turn out to be.

Perhaps it would've sat there,
four-square, for the Frog Poet,
but when I bent to finger

the Braille of its back with second-
hand affections, it shot off
into the squatting queue of cars.

Held now by their lights,
and Buster Keaton white,
I bobbed between them

after my revved up quarry
like someone caught on a TV
shoot-out. At the very last

I risked offence and grasped
the sand-filled sock of a frog,
no sooner into the action

than spiralling out of it,
as the traffic began to flow;
the frog no sooner mine

than it was leaping the wall
onto the front lawn of a Home
for the Elderly, leaving me,

a split second, frozen
in drizzle, offering an invisible
bouquet to the silent stars.

122

C.J. Roberts

## WITCHES' BUTTER AND BRAIN FUNGUS

Jaz liked to think that her homework desk would not have looked out of place in the corporate headquarters of a successful bank or insurance company. It was a model of businesslike elegance and authority. Smooth, black-painted wood shone warmly from regular polishing. She leaned back and surveyed it from the green, high-backed executive chair, the top of the range.

The desk's working surface was satisfyingly free from any suggestion of clutter. Jaz was simply not the type of teenager to dump her clothes just anywhere, to leave her papers unsorted or drop an earring where it was not supposed to go. Things had their proper places and observing the rules kept the whole thing in balance. She liked to echo her father: anyone could be born clever, but to be really efficient you had to have a system. Order, purpose and discipline were his watchwords and hers too, especially today.

A plastic desk-tidy sat at the back, its pipe-organ tubes filled with carefully sorted paper clips, pens, pencils and rubbers. Next to this was a large, black stapler, a small box of tissues and a black sellotape dispenser. A green-shaded banker's lamp shone onto a brown leather blotter, a gift from one of Daddy's clients.

Even out of sight, everything had its place. Folded cardboard inserts kept envelopes, writing paper and notelets from becoming muddled. School work was rigidly segregated from personal material. The file drawer was organised both in alphabetical order and colour coded by subject for ease of cross-reference.

Today, however, she faced a writing task which presented her system with a real challenge. Though personal, it demanded to be carried out as carefully and professionally as a formal letter. Though emotional, it had to be controlled, even somewhat detached if the feelings she wished to convey were to come through with clarity.

Jaz took one of the large pads of lined A4 paper from her school drawer and selected a black fibre-tip pen from the desk-tidy. Satisfied with her choice of materials, she wrote:

Margaret Kilbride
A Eulogy
by her friend
Jasmine Andrews

She had consulted her dictionary, which told her that *eulogy* was an Americanism when applied to a dead person, but she preferred it to *epitaph* or *in memoriam*. These were words for dead bones under a cold, mossy stone. If you wanted only to mourn a person's death, they would do. But if you were to stand up and say aloud what their life had meant to you, *eulogy* felt right.

She was less certain of the word *friend*. Was that overstating things? After all, she and Mags had only known one another, what, three or four months at most. Jaz considered the alternatives. *Classmate* was juvenile. *Colleague* made them sound like civil servants. *Schoolfriend* might be better. She decided to leave the word for now, but come back to it when she was finished.

At the top right corner of the page, she wrote:

First Draft.

Then she faced the problem of how to address the audience. Or what did you call them at a funeral service? Congregation? If she started with *Ladies and gentlemen* it would sound like she was about to kick off a bad variety act.

*Ladies and gentlemen, a funny thing happened on the way to the crematorium, no, please, missus, don't ...*

Jaz found that she was smiling and checked herself. She mustn't let her mind wander. This was important.

She could always start on an informal note:

*Friends ...*

Too sugary, she decided. And what if some of them weren't her friends? What if there were people there she'd never met? They might resent her implied chumminess at such an occasion. There was always the religious option:

*Dearly Beloved ...*

No, that was what the minister would be saying, wasn't it? Best not tread on the Church's toes. Perhaps she could seek advice once the rest of the speech was ready. In the meantime she would start straight in, to hit the ground running as Daddy was always saying.

She looked out of the window, collecting her thoughts, steeling herself. It looked like it would be another beautiful day of Indian summer. Early morning rain had given way to a light, hazy mist and even now you could sense the sun almost breaking through. By lunchtime it would be bright and warm.

Jaz tried to form a picture of Margaret in her mind. She visualised her as she had first seen her, wearing their terrible, drab, dark grey and navy school uniform, shuffling her feet awkwardly in her broad shoes. Her myopic squint peeped anxiously at the front of the class during morning registration. Mr Collins had said something to her quietly and she had smiled shyly.

Jaz leant forward and wrote:

I did not have the chance to know Margaret Kilbride very well or for very long. But I wanted to say something today about the Mags that I knew, that all of her friends at St Bartholomew's knew, and about why we will miss her.

I remember the day she arrived at our school. Mr Collins introduced her to the class. As her family had moved close to my parents' house, I had already been asked to be her school buddy, showing her around and introducing her to people to ease her in until she made her own friends. So I had a special reason, perhaps, for wishing to take a close look at this new girl who now stood before us.

Jaz paused for a moment, searching for a way to describe her first impressions in words which would not be likely to upset Mags's parents. She saw again the lumpy, clumsy figure standing next to the teacher's desk, her frizzy red hair pulled severely back from a broad, pimply brow. She saw the pathetic, *please-don't-eat-me* smile as Mags's thin lips pulled back to show her large, horsy teeth. She saw her swaying on her flat feet, obviously not knowing what to do with her hands – first clasping them, then folding her arms, putting them behind her back, the whole sequence an unconscious, spastic jive. Above all you just thought how big she was. How awkward-looking and gallumphing and *big*.

This would need careful phrasing.

At first, I wasn't at all certain whether I was going to like this new girl. But there was something very touching, very open about her. Something you could not help liking. I could see straight away that she was not at ease that first morning, that she was a shy and sensitive person, someone who at that moment was feeling unbearably self-conscious.

And with good reason, too, Jaz could have added. Still, she felt she had managed to get the point across without causing offence.

During the course of that day, and of the days and weeks that followed, I got to know Margaret – Mags as I quickly began to call her – about as well as I could say I know anyone. We discovered many things in common. Similar tastes in music, in clothes, in books and in films and in

Jaz stopped and looked at the list she had just composed.
Men.
That was the missing word. Similar tastes in men.

and in lots of other things as well.

Although she told me that at first she did feel quite homesick, she settled in well at school and I believe she quickly grew to feel at home here. She had a love of the countryside, which she was able to express in long walks we shared together in the woods and the hills around our homes. During these walks we would swap stories, look out for deer and squirrels and sometimes confide secret things to one another, the way you will with a friend you have learned to love and to trust.

A tear splashed onto the page and Jaz was surprised to find that she was crying. She grabbed a tissue from the box and sat back, sniffing. She blew her nose and looked out of the window again. The mist was all but gone and the sun was breaking through strongly now. Perfect mushroom-picking weather. It was a day to be glad to be alive, not suffocating in morbid thoughts. She needed to keep her wits about her if she was to get this job done.

They were so alike, that was part of the problem. Too alike to be close friends for long really. At first it was fun to find someone who thought the same, felt the same, who even began to dress the same out of school. But after a while it got so claustrophobic you could hardly breathe. How do you get that into your eulogy?

How do you get the whole person in there if you don't allow for the times when she was an absolute pain in the behind? Are you going to put in how she never knew when she wasn't wanted? Or how pathetic she was around Mr Collins, who obviously was never going to fancy her in a million years, not even if she was the last woman left alive? Are you going to say how you joined in with them chanting *Mags is a slag* that time until she locked herself in the seniors' loo, or how sometimes you were so sick of her sticking to you like she was your shadow that you could quite easily have pushed her off the bloody bridge yourself?

Feeling light-headed, Jaz swivelled her chair around and looked over her room. Everywhere her eyes travelled, different objects called up various memories. There was her keyboard where she and Mags had practised their favourite songs, only somehow the songs you liked best were always the hardest ones to play. A couple of the books in the bookcase were Mags's. And the pile of magazines on the bottom shelf contained numerous quizzes they had filled in together. *How Do I Know if He's Cheating? Is Your Man a Peter Pan? Are YOU a Sex-Bomb ... or a Damp Squib?*

The weird thing was that they always got exactly the same score in these quizzes. Category Two. They were the people who weren't exactly doomed to miss the party, but were probably going to be in the room next door when it was happening. Or maybe, as one of the magazines put it, your invitation just got held up in the post.

Jaz's eye fell on the book of mushroom types they had pored over together. Jaz's daddy had taught her all about mushrooms, from where to look to find the best ones to how to cook the ones you brought home and she had begun to share her knowledge with Mags. They had lain on their bellies on Jaz's bed, flipping through the book and rejoicing in some of the baroque names the different species had been given. Candle-Snuff and Dead Man's Fingers and Jew's Ear and Witches' Butter and Brain Fungus.

There were many edible mushrooms in the woods and meadows bordering the town. Jaz's favourite was the Chanterelle, the soft yellow-brown mushroom which nature had designed to resemble perfectly the fallen leaf of the birch tree and which you found growing under moss at the feet of some birches. Chanterelles had the most marvellous woody aroma, had the appearance of soft calves' leather and when cooked with a little butter and garlic, well, as Daddy said, there was nothing better. They appeared in the autumn and the best time to harvest them, Jaz told Mags, was in sunshine following rainfall.

Jaz turned back to her desk and picked up her pen again.

I was with Margaret the day of her

Yes, now you're getting to it, she thought. The day of her what exactly? Her death? Direct, Jaz thought, but insensitive. Passing away? Untimely demise?

I was with Margaret on the day of her tragic accident. We had gone mushroom picking in the woods that border the line of the railway embankment. It was a walk we had shared many times over the summer. We separated to hunt for different species. Why she strayed as far as the bridge, I cannot imagine. We both knew how dangerous it was and had been warned not to go near there.

The picture came into Jaz's mind of Mags lying, face up, back broken, on the big rock in the middle of the fast-flowing stream, the wind blowing her red hair wildly back and forward over her face like a flag, blood staining the rock, her body obviously lifeless. She heard her own voice crying out. Mags! Mags! No!

It was not Mags I found lying there. Only a shell of Mags, which had once contained Mags. Mags is gone, I know, to a better place and she would want us to be happy for her.

A bit clichéd, but what else could you do? She liked *is gone* much better than *has gone*. That was a nice touch.

Jaz laid her pen down just as the doorbell rang. She listened to her mother's footsteps crossing from the kitchen through the downstairs hall as she locked the A4 pad carefully away in her personal drawer.

'Jasmine,' her mother called upstairs. 'It's for you.'

'Coming,' Jaz replied, clicking off the banker's lamp.

Her palms were sweating. She wiped them on the legs of her jeans, then stood up and looked at herself in the full-length wardrobe mirror. No damage from the tears earlier. She put her shoulders back, drew a deep breath and left the room.

Jaz's mother met her at the kitchen door.

'I've asked her if she'd like a coffee, but she says you two have made plans to go for a walk,' she said.

'Uh-huh,' said Jaz.

She leaned into the kitchen and smiled at Mags, who was sitting at the table, looking big and myopic in an awful floral-print dress.

'Did you bring something to carry the mushrooms home in?'

Mags hoisted up a battered old sports bag.

'That'll do,' Jaz said. 'Let me get my coat and I'm ready.'

James Robertson

## DON'T START ME TALKIN'
## (I'LL TELL EVERYTHING I KNOW)

The woman looked to be in her fifties. On her head was a grey helmet of tight curls. She had the face of a smoker who has been giving up for decades. It seemed to take her an age to shuffle up to the sales counter.

The shop was quiet, in fact apart from the two of them it was completely empty.

George Johnstone had heard her shoes on the steps outside, and had come out from behind the counter and moved over to the jazz section. He sorted a few CD cases into alphabetical order with a practised air and walked over to her.

'Can I help you?' he asked.

She looked at him hopelessly.

'I'll tell you what it is, son. I've been having a terrible time lately and I just thought if I could get some new music into my life it would help. I want something ... well, I just want something with feeling.'

'With feeling,' said George.

'Ay. Somehow all my old records aren't having the right effect. And I thought I'd come in and spend a few bob on something with a bit of feeling.'

'A few bob.'

'Ay, in a manner of speaking.'

George considered her face. On the one hand, he really did not have time for this. On the other, he had all the time in the world. He saw such despair in the lines around her eyes that he feared she might burst into tears.

'What kind of music do you like?' he asked.

She shrugged. 'That's what I want to know. That's where I thought someone like you could help me.'

'You want me to tell you what kind of music you like?'

She looked more optimistic. 'Ay, could you?' She looked at him directly for the first time and he half turned away. 'Are you all right, son?'

'Ay,' he said, managing a smile.

'You're shaking,' she said.

'Touch of the flu,' he muttered. He held out his right hand, palm outwards, fingers extended, and looked at its trembling. He remembered learning that men and women inspected their fingernails differently. He'd read it in some detective novel when he was about thirteen and going through puberty. He'd learnt then that he did it the female way. He still did, although he'd tried to change. Now he turned the hand round, closed the fingers into the palm and the trembling stopped.

'That's better,' he said.

'You should be in your bed,' said the woman.

'Ay, well.' He shrugged. 'Tell me, then, what *don't* you like?'

The woman thought about it.

'This weather,' she said. 'It gets you down. And Christmas, that did my head in. I don't like Christmas.'

'I meant musically,' said George. 'Anyway, Christmas was weeks ago. It'll be spring any day.'

'Ay, but what difference does that make? You've still to pay for it, don't you? From before. I've not finished yet and now there's all the birthdays. It's never-ending, just one thing after another.'

'Look,' said George, 'forget about all that. It's only money. Tell me about music. Musically, what do you want? Something to make you feel happy?'

'Not necessarily. I wouldn't want to buy a record just to make myself happy, it might not work, and then where would I be? I don't care what kind of mood it puts me in. I just want something with feeling.'

'What about the blues? That's mostly what's here.'

She looked at him uncomprehendingly.

'The blues. Blues music.'

'What's that then? Has it got feeling?'

He decided to play some blues for her. There was still nobody else in the shop and although he knew he should get her out and get going, he felt like listening to some blues himself. The shop-keys were on a ring in his pocket. He went and locked the door. 'We're closed,' he said to her with a smile. 'I'll take you on a wee guided tour of the blues.'

He was a bit concerned that she'd used the word 'record' when there was nothing but cassettes and compact discs on the racks, but he didn't want to worry her about that straightaway. He felt it would humiliate her.

He selected some CD cases and went to the shelves behind the counter to find the discs. It was a good cataloguing system, it didn't take him long. Then he started putting music through the speakers; some harp, some guitar, some Delta, some Chicago, some folk blues, some electric. He played some Muddy Waters and some Lightnin' Hopkins, some Freddie King and some Sonny Boy Williamson. He played 'Black Cadillac' and 'Don't Start Me Talkin'' and 'Sad Letter Blues'. He pulled up a moulded plastic chair for the woman, and gave her a blast of Howlin' Wolf and a sample of Willie Dixon, some Blind Lemon Jefferson and Son House, some Bessie Smith, Big Mama Thornton and Etta James. Hell, after a while he hardly needed to play the songs, he just said the names, while the woman sat and nodded, rocking against the give in the chairback, and blew long streams of smoke from her nostrils. John Lee Hooker, Robert Johnson, Big Bill Broonzy, Leadbelly. The names crowded into the atmosphere and hung there. George and the woman talked a little, and he gently explained that it was very difficult to buy records any more, most of the music companies had simply stopped making them. While they talked, her cigarette filters gathered in an old polystyrene cup he'd found under the counter. Outside, the world grew dark.

Then it was time to go.

'Oh God,' she said. 'I'll need to get back and put their tea on. I'm sorry I can't buy anything, after all that. I'm so out of touch. I feel like I've wasted your afternoon.'

'No,' he said, 'it was important to do this. It's good to slow down sometimes. And I'm sorry they don't make records any more. There's something about vinyl you just can't beat.' He was putting all the CDs away carefully, and returning the empty cases to the racks.

'Ay, you're right there,' she said. 'These new things are all right, I suppose, they're unbreakable and that, but they sound just as scratchy to me.'

'That's the recordings,' he said. 'Some of these are sixty years old, maybe more.'

'Tell me about it,' she said. She began her painful shuffle towards the door. By the time she got there he'd tidied everything away, put the keys back in the till-drawer. 'I'm coming out with you,' he said. He held the door for her. 'Mind on your way up, there's a loose step.'

'Thanks for being so patient,' she said, buttoning her shapeless coat against the chill wind. 'It must be nice, having your own record shop.'

'Ay,' he said, 'I suppose so.' He pulled the door behind him, made sure it was properly shut, the way it had been when he came in. Only then did he realise he'd forgotten to take the CD he'd put aside. But it was too late. The spell was broken. He wouldn't go back in there alone.

The woman was halfway to the pavement. He waited till she'd got there, then went briskly up the steps and hurried off in the opposite direction.

*

He'd never noticed the shop before, although he must have walked along the street dozens of times. The sign, BASEMENT BEAT, was obscure and dirty. He'd only spotted it because it was a day when he was looking at everything. Details. This was a way of asking himself what he was doing there, if not being there would make any difference. One of the stone steps shoogled when he descended. He turned the handle of the door.

It was after three o'clock now, the day was starting to fade. For a place that didn't appear to be doing much business it was surprisingly well stocked. Maybe that was why. He wondered how much money you'd need to take in a day just to stay afloat. Two, three hundred, if you ran it single-handed? Maybe more.

George quickly understood that it was a specialist shop. Jazz, blues, R&B, soul. He didn't know much about jazz, but blues, that was his thing, and there was stacks of it. Nothing much from the Hit Parade. He almost said it out loud. The place had a gloomy, old-fashioned atmosphere that made a phrase like that seem appropriate. And the oddest thing, for a music shop – it was in absolute silence. He looked around. No customers. No staff either. It was as if everybody had gone out for a tea-break and forgotten to lock the door.

He flicked through a few CDs. They made a slapping sound against one another, advertising his presence. But no one came through the doorway behind the counter. He began to feel the need for something on the sound system. The speakers stared down at him like security cameras.

He saw a Johnny Shines album he'd been wanting for years. The sticker said £12.99. He couldn't really afford it but he'd probably never see it again. He carried the empty CD case up to the counter and coughed.

After a minute he said, 'Hello? Anybody in?' His voice was startling in the silence. He felt like he shouldn't be there. He stepped around the counter and leaned through the doorway into the back room.

The shop owner was a man maybe in his sixties. He had thick black-framed spectacles and strands of sandy hair plastered over his bald head. One strand had come loose and hung like a bell-pull over his right eye, brushing the lens of his glasses. He wore an open-necked shirt and the waistcoat from a pinstripe suit. He was slumped in a chair behind a desk and the desk prevented George from seeing if he wore pinstripe trousers as well.

'Hello?' said George. But he realised that the man was not sleeping but dead.

His arms hung at his sides, his chin was resting on his chest, framed by the V of his shirt. In front of him was an opened can of cola and a half-eaten sandwich resting on a baker's paper poke.

George felt a curious calm wash through him. He crossed the floor of the room knowing that there was no urgency, no need to panic. He touched the man's cheek with the back of his hand. The skin had a cool clammy feel. He picked up the can and felt from its weight that it was about half full. When he held it to his ear he could hear the faint ping of almost expired fizz.

Heart attack, he thought. Maybe. He wasn't a doctor. There was no sign of violence or disturbance. It looked like the shop owner had just died sitting there eating his piece. George glanced at the sandwich. He could see the ragged curve of the man's tooth-marks where he had bitten through grated cheese and pickle.

He went back into the shop. From behind the counter it seemed even emptier. He himself had been the sole customer, now he was gone. He realised that he was still clutching the Johnny Shines case. He laid it down on the counter.

The cash register was switched on, the green display reading 0.00. George pressed the no sale button but the machine started whining. He pressed the cancel button. He tapped in 12.99, rang it up as a sale, then tapped in the same figures as cash tendered and pressed the sale button. The till drawer sprang open and a receipt was printed.

There wasn't much money in there. Two ten-pound notes, a fiver, nine pound coins and some other change. George lifted the tray out and looked in the drawer. There was a little pile of notes and cheques at the back. He counted five twenties and seven tens and put them in his pocket. He put the cheques back and replaced the tray. He took the thirty-four pounds from the plastic compart-ments, then put back the fiver and eight pounds. He took a penny in change and put it with the other money in his pocket. In one of the compartments was a bunch of keys. He took it out and closed the till. He tore off the receipt and dropped it on the floor.

He thought about walking home. But he didn't want to go home. He shared a flat with two other people. Whether he went back there or not he would be neither missed nor noticed. Sometimes several days would pass when he wouldn't see one or other of his flatmates. Sometimes he wouldn't see either of them. He never wondered where they were, if they were safe or in trou-ble. He knew that, for them, the same applied to himself. If he closed the door of his room and stayed in there for a week they wouldn't know or care. This was supposed to make him feel free.

He was ten minutes' brisk walk to the train station. And the bus station. He thought of cities in England he could go to. Places he'd never been before. Manchester, Birmingham, Leeds, Bristol. Beautifully anonymous-sounding places. He wanted to walk through a crowd on an unfamiliar street.

He went back through to the office. The body hadn't moved. He remembered reading a Western when he was a boy, in which a corpse had suddenly sat up and groaned, terrifying everybody except for the hero, who knew that this was what corpses some-times did.

He tried to imagine what it was like to be alone in a room with a dead man. He tried to see himself in a book or a movie. Outside there were the sounds of cars and buses rolling by, the tapping of women's brisk heels and, in the distance, the cry of a siren. Inside there was the desk, some shelves loaded with files and catalogues, a stack of mail-order forms. There was another table on which sat an electric kettle, a couple of mugs, a spoon with a brown tide-mark, an assortment of tea bags, sugar, milk. George lifted the can of cola and drank from it, feeling its warm flat sweetness against his throat.

He felt as if he and the shop owner were special, as if they shared something denied to everybody else. He wondered what the man's last thoughts had been.

He wondered what was the last ever piece of music the man had heard. He went to check the sound system, but there wasn't a CD in it. He thought again how strange that was, for a music shop. Just then he heard someone coming down the steps.

*

The woman trailed her way back across the city. She had been out all day. She didn't want to go home but she knew she would. Somebody had to feed them. She would need to stop in the Co-op on the way for some messages: beans, tatties, chops. She could hear the grill spitting and hissing at her as she cooked them.

She crossed the river by the pedestrian bridge. If you were on it and somebody else was coming from the other side it bounced you, made you feel like you had new energy in your soles. She liked the feel of it. Sometimes she'd stop halfway across and let the energy of other folk throb into her.

It was almost night. The lights of the city gleamed like amber fish in the black water. The clouds overhead threatened more rain, more cold. She hated this time of year. It clenched you up, turned you grey inside. There was no mercy in it.

The river was full, it rushed beneath her towards the sea. She watched a ripple in it that caught the reflection of the lamp behind her. The ripple was constantly turning like a rope; always new water, always the same shape. She could feel people passing behind her, the bridge going up and down.

She felt utterly alone.

The music had been unlike anything she'd ever heard, and yet she felt she recognised it. She'd not understood the rhythms of some of it, hadn't been able to pick out all the words that were moaned, wailed, screamed, muttered. Some of it had sounded like ghosts coming from a long time ago. But one thing she knew: it had feeling. Oh, ay, the young fellow had been right about that.

Songs like that made you want to start walking and never stop. They made you want to lie down and sleep. They made you want a drink, a greet, a laugh. The people who made those songs, she thought, they didn't wake up in the morning and wonder what to sing about. The stuff was in them, *was* them. It just came pouring out.

She was going back there, definitely. Tomorrow, or if not tomorrow the next day. She wanted to get a CD player so she could take some of the music home with her. Or one with headphones, so you could sit on a bus and travel with it in your ears. She wanted to ask the guy in the shop where to start, who to listen to first.

She looked down into the black swirling water and felt she was on the edge of discovering something.

**Dilys Rose**

# WINDSONG

```
si   si   si
   moo   moo
      si  si  si
         moo   moo
      moomsi si  moomsi
   moomoo si  moomoo
         moom   moom
si si  si simoo   si si si simoo

s    i    m    o    o    m


                  har harma har
                matt matta atta
                  harma tt tt tt
                harma tt tt tt
            ma ma ma arma
            ma ma ma arma
      harm harm
att att att   atta
attan   attan
         har harma har
      ma ma har ma ma
         harma ma harma
                ma ma tan arma
                  tanta har matta

h    a    r    m    a    t    t    a    n


bb bb bb  sssssssss
ss bi ss bi ss bi
bi  bi  bi
 bi  bi  bi
   bibi   bibi
      se se
         bibi   bibi
            sssssss

         b    i    s    e
```

tra ra ra ramo
  tra ra ra ramo
    ramon ramon
              montane   montane
              tramont    tramonte tramonte ontane
  onta tan   onta
    onta tan onta
      rama tan rama
        tan tan tan
                tram
          tan tan tan
                    tram
            tramo tramonte
          tramo tramonte
        tantra  mon tantra
tantra mon tantra
      tramont tramont
                montane   montane
        ram
            tra
              amo mont amo
                tantramo tan
                tantramo tan

t     r     a     m     o     n     t     a     n     e


si si si siro
  si si si siro
    rocco si rocco   rocco si iro
                iro si siro iro si siro
        roc roc roc roccsi rocc rocc rocc roccsi
          si rocc rocc si rocc
            rocco occ occo
                    occsi si occo co occo si occsi
          si siro si siro ro iro si iro si rocc si rocc rocc rocc
            rocc rocc rocc
                  rocc rocc rocc
              sisi
          sisi

s     i     r     o     c     c     o

is is is ist
 is is is ist
  is mis is mist
   is mist is mistra
mis mis mis mistra
 mist mist
ra ra ra
tra ra ra
ra ra ra
ral al al
ral a ral al a
ral a al a

tt tt tt   tt tt tt

mist

        ist

                        is

                    is

            s

        s

m     i     s     t     r     a     l

chi chi
chin chin

chi chi
chin chin

chino chi
chino
chino chi
chi

nook chi
chi nook
nook chi
 chi  chin

chin chi chi
chin chi
chin chi chi
chin chi

nook nook
chin chin
chino chi
 chino

chi chi nook
chi chi
nook nook
chi nook chi

c    h    i    n    o    o    k

Suhayl Saadi

# SAMHAIN

The awd mon finished aff the last dregs ae the glais, inspected it then tossed his heid back and tried tae sip some mair, tae tease oot the dregs ae the dregs. The last, desperate draps ae malt. The glais clanged agin the boa'tle, empty on empty. Nae echo. Jis an odour. He slumped back in his chair and let his lids slide shut. Ootside the bothan, the snaw climbed thick upon the dykes and the nicht creaked wi the soo ae nuhin. It wis the middle ae nuwhur, haufway up a beinn and the stars so bricht it wisnae dark at aw an the muin up there above the awd mon's heid like a virgin's cunt. Unbraken. Perfect roon. Skimin, drappin its licht over the laun, the bothan, the awd mon, his fuskie boa'tle, his teem glais, his great shocka lang white hair. Had been reid wance. Aye, wance on a day. Enough ae that. Memories. O Goad, memories.

He opened his ees an went over tae the grill. Took oot a spunk an lunt the ring. The gas flared up on the third attempt, almost burning the side ae his hond. He licked the skin. Deid flesh, the taste ae him. He slapped a pan ontae the ring and looked fur some mulk. It took him a guid while tae find ony, so that when at last he tuimed it in, it bizzed an sizzled and sent the waff ae burnin up his snoot. Burnin mulk. Burnin flesh. Same as the stink ae snaw ootside, aw aroon, everywhur. The stink beneath the smell, the deid leaves under the snaw. The scent ae the stars an the muin. He had the urge tae go oot an walk in the saft snaw mar fhear-allabain, tae wander in the frozen nicht and tae nivir come back. Tae lose himsel in the past. The bad ault past. Leavin the bainne in the pan, he went tae the door. The fallin-doon, brak door. The bothan wis gae ramshackle, hudnae bin cleant up fur decades. It wis whit he hud sunk tae, the awd mon, it wis aw that wis left after a life had passed. After aw his sins were accountet fur. Aw fuck, so many sins. He twisted the hannle. It wis stuck. It didnae bloody work. Even that wis fawing apart. He sighed, his putrid awd lichts sighed, blowin oot thur air stagnant wi seeventie Samhains, aye there wis air in those lungs, in the guts a those lungs that hud neer been braithed. Deid air. Wis braithed in at birth an wuid be braithed oot at daith. In the daith-rattle. But he widnae hear it. His lug would be as deid as the beinn oot there. He shoved the door open and stood in the door-check, in a circle ae shadee or wis it a circle ae licht. He wisnae sure. It wis lichter ootside than it hud been in the bothan, whit wi the muin an the stairs booncin aff the snaw. There wis nae wind, so the shadees didnae blow away. He could smell them. Heich above him rose the great dark bulk ae the beinn, its shooders so sheer that no snaw, no even a flichan wis able tae cling tae the hard rock-face. It hud aw been licht that, even back fifty winters ago when the awd mon hud first come tae the bothan. It wis different then. He wis young, the world wis new, his sins were no sae lang. Or at least, they hudnae seemed tae maitter. He'd come theer wi a leddy, aye, a lang-haired, tall, beautiful leddy an they'd danced ootside in the snaw tae the soon ae the binneas whisperin across the beanntan aw the way fae the fur West whur the dubhlachd came fae aye an they'd lain thegether in the dry snaw, lomnochd and her drùis had met an mingled wi his drùis an her fit hud banged doon on the hard snaw like the hammer ae the Cailleach, the awd wumin ae winter an the traneens fur aff hud creaked an split wi the soon ae their roupin. O Goad that wis heiven heiven that wis. The wumin wis awreedie mairrit but he hudnae cairt. Nor hud she, fur that maitter. He recalt the hollow a wee bit up the beinn whur they'd done it aye he wis able tae picture it even then, fuftie years on. It wis on th'other side ae the beinn, overlookin the black an the rocks and the spume. An aw the craigs covert in tangle an badderlock. An the cavern whur th'awd wifies said the roane came tae sow thur seed every Samhain an you could hear them because thur roups wur no like ony ae the sea-birds an no like folk eether. It wis a roar like the blaw ae Saint Michael's horn at the gates ae Judgement Day. An they'd heard it, him'n the wumin, as they climbed tae the summit tae the hollow jist in the shooder ae the summit aye an their ane roup hud mingled wi the cries ae the roin and the roupin hud become wan an it wis gae the best moment ae his hale life, naw, it wis the best. In the bothan, the bainne wis beilin over but the awd mon didnae hear nocht he wis saunterin up the beinn tae look fur the roin aye he wis ayeways a radge wan a bloody radge wan aye so the awd wumin had said whun he geed big Bridie a babe at aleeven, aye she was gae big fur her age but no as big as she got, nine twenty-seevens thence. And noo th'awd bastart-faither wis clamberin up the beinn, the door a broken jaw behind his back but he no carin no gien a dang cause he's nivir gien a dang aboot onything but jist shrugged his shooders aw his life richt from the stert. A callous bastart, him wi his rid hair, aye lang locks ae it there in the snaw, fawin across the face ae the marrit wumin, across her ees fou a love, aye no jis druis no like him. The snaw sleid an sklyted beneath the soles ae his scuddie fit cause he hudnae ony sheas left tae wear. He wis in a state ae dire penury. Everything he ever had, wis loast. Had been mooted awa bit by bit, over the years till this fallen-doon bothan wis aw he had an noo wi its door wide open tae the warld. Thur wis no one, nae souch the nicht an the snaw lay as peaceful as deith an it wisnae peaceful at aw, naw no fur those left behind, onyhow. Mibee fur the deid. Mibee. Mibee no. The grun wis beginnin tae rise mair steeply an bits ae ice had begun tae form on tap ae the snaw so that th'awd mon's baries were slippin an slidin an noo he wis on his knees an honds, his palms, the luifs that had clasped the marrit wumin's fingers wi her ring her gauden ring that had been her grannie's she said rubbin agin his huil his virginal white huil she'd changed honds aye it wis her richt hond the ring wis on. Aw fuck, he realised, fifty years intae the unknown but what he'd thocht wis known wisnae and whit did it mean? He paused there, on the snowy dorchadas ae the beinn, the sloped licht dorchadas an he wis balancin on the white balancin like it wis a tightrope fur fuck's sake aye an below him fell the geodha, the lang creek whose ent wis the ocean the invisible watter where the roin rouped ivverie Samhain nicht an the faeries ae the land, ae the tide ae the land came an matet wi the roin in great tuinn an the linnets screamin overheid, screamin an spunkin up there in the dark sky. An the awd mon climbed higher an higher in the frozen air an he thocht at wan point he could hear the neighin ae the winter mare an by that he knew he wis shankin widdershins O fuck but he didnae know how he knew but somehow deep inside his heid, his aged heid stuffed wi nuhin but putrefaction because the beinn had three heids, three huidit heids an as he looked back, the trees had shrunk tae scrunts, deid scrunts which still (ein though they wur deid) spelt oot a nem an it wis his nem but it wisnae, naw it wisnae in letters but it wis the shape ae his fate the ogham ae his weird O Goad he wis gan tae dee but he wisnae dowie naw you couldnae be sad aboot destiny it wisnae avoidable, it wis you an yer ancestors aw the fuckin lot ae them, wan fuck intae the next, a lang line ae tadgers aw stieve an thrustin an hot. Naw, no hot, calt like the nicht, cho fuar ris a' phuinnsein cause now the awd mon wis nearly there, near as dang it tae the heicht to whur he hud tae be, whur he hud always had tae be, tae hear the strings ae the clarsach that haud played oot his life. The three chords ae oige, adulthuid and eild; the three martyrdoms, white, green and rid; the three dieths.

> *Ebbtide tae me as ae the sea!*
>   *Awd age causes me tae reproach …*
> *Ah am th'awd wumin ae Beare,*
>   *An ivir-new smock Ah used tae wear:*
> *Today – such is ma mean estate –*
>   *Ah wear no even a cast-aff smock …*
> *O happy the isle ae the great sea*
>   *Which the flood reaches after th' ebb!*
> *As for me, Ah do not expect*
>   *Flood after ebb tae come tae me*

An the bainne wis beilin in the dorchadas but the awd mon didnae care he didnae care cause it wis aw written onyway an he wis tae get tae see it aw written, in the trees, the stocs, a' bheinn lom, the slidin snaw. In his aine hert. Aye, fur the first time he wis gazin intae his aine hert an its duibhre, an its darkness wis a peak, a summit, mullach na beinne, an fae there he wuid see it aw, his life an the lives ae the many. The wumin wi her grannie's ring on the wrang hond, the weann withoot a ma an a faither, a' bheinn lom-nochd ann an abhainn na h-oidhche. Jis like Dante, he wuid see his dan traced oot fae the toap ae the beinn. The awd mon wisnae cault ony mair he wisnae shiverin, no in his airms no in his hert. He wis warum, beilin like the bainne. An the flames slaiked the iron pan, the awd wood ae the bothan, yella flames like great big tadgers makin the wood glow an creak an curl an the awd mon ripped aaf his claes an ran thru the snaw jis like a young carle, climbin, climbin aw the while. The muin wis fu, fu as the iron chord which keeps aw the faeries, aw the awd yins awa, sends them back intae thur dark broch an hauds them there aw through the great Samhain. Aye an he needit tae leap intae the braw muir, the big braw sea, black as it wis, blacker than heil, cause he'd treatit her bad, that wumin, he'd taken her awa fae her mon an then dumped her cause he didnae want tied doon an he said tae her it wis on acoont ae her no knowin what she wantit but it wis a lie so the truth here on the back ae this big black beinn wis that he didnae feel fur onyone. No even fur himsel. He nivir had.

Aw ae a sudden, the snaw vanished an there wis nuhin but big, black moothfu's ae nicht air. The awd mon stopped. Listened tae the boomin soon ae the waves as they bled agin the rocks. An rubha lom. He didnae look back, but felt it. The bothan, the end ae him, burnin bricht in the white. Didnae see it but knew the last bits ae his mortal coil were shiftin themselves aff ae the earthly plane. Didnae look back but heard his dan mapped oot in great chords ae white, his ages, the fowk he wis, air on stone, soul on flesh. An he wis himsel astride the wumin in the snaw, and he wis roupin wi his rid hair streamin an his tadger stiff as a deid mon and she wis roupin wi her thighs spreid an her cunt wide open. An he wis the wee boy in the coille, rubbin himsel against the big stonin stane, feelin the mon spume oot ae him in great, hoat gouts. An he wis the awd mon in his bothan, still feelin nuhin, knowin less an his bothan wis burnin, burnin it wis an he wis burnin wi it fur it wis the only way. An aon shlighe, the wan strewn wi briars an bracken but the true wan. Then he heard a whooshin, no wi his lugs but wi his banes an he knew it wis the faery fowk come tae wisk him aff an he felt a great, black warmth wrap itsel roun him an he took a step forwards an he wis over the edge an intae the allt.

## GAELIC WORDS:

| | |
|---|---|
| a' bheinn lom | the barren mountain |
| a' bheinn lomnochd ann an abhainn na h-oidhche | the mountain naked in the river of night |
| abhainn | river |
| allt | stream |
| am muir | (the) sea |
| an aon shlighe | the one road, way |
| an rubha lom | the bare rock |
| bainne | milk |
| beanntan | hills, mountains |
| beinn | mountain |
| binneas | melody |
| bothan | hut/farmhands' living quarters |
| braw muir | big braw sea |
| breagha | beautiful, pretty |
| breine *(brehyna)* | putrefaction |
| broch *(broch)* | hill-fort |
| cho fuar ris a' phuinnsein | as cold as the poison |
| clarsach | Celtic harp |
| coille | forest |
| dan | destiny, fate |
| dorchadas | darkness, blackness |
| drùis | lust |
| dubh | black |
| dubhlachd | gloom, winter, December |
| duibhre | darkness |
| geal | white |
| geodha | creek |
| lomnochd | naked |
| mar fhear-allabain | like a wanderer |
| mullach | summit |
| ogham | occult manner of ancient Gaelic writing, formed on a proto-telegraphic system by so many strokes for each letter, above or below a stem line, which was often formed by the angle of a stone monument |
| oige | youth |
| ròin | seals (maybe mermaids and mermen) |
| ròn | seal |
| rubha | promontory |
| Samhain | Feast of All Souls |
| slighe | path, road |
| stocs | trunks |
| tuinn | waves |

## SCOTS WORDS:

| | |
|---|---|
| baries | (in) bare feet |
| brak | broken |
| badderlock | edible seaweed |
| braw | fine |
| broch | fairy mound |
| calt | cold |
| carle | young man |
| dang | damn!; to knock, beat, strike |
| dowie | sad |
| dyke | country wall |
| eild | old age |
| flichan | snowflake |
| fowk | folk |
| fuskie | whisky |
| gae | quite |
| heicht | high |
| huidit | hooded |
| huil | skin |
| lichts | lights |
| lug | ear |
| luifs | palms |
| lunt | a match, light |
| mon | man |
| mooted | frittered away |
| muir | moor |
| nocht | nothing |
| radge | mad, furious |
| roupin | roaring, shouting |
| scrunts | shrivelled stems |
| scuddie | naked |
| shankin | walking |
| sklyted | the way a soft, half-liquid mass moves, messily |
| slaiked | licked, slobbered on |
| souch | (the sound of the wind) |
| spunk | a spark, a match |
| stieve | firm, strong |
| tadgers | penises |
| teemed | hungry, empty, echoing |
| thocht | thought |
| tuimed | emptied |
| weird | fate, destiny |

Ian Stephen

## HIS MAJESTY'S YACHT *IOLAIRE*
## (formerly *AMALTHEA*)

*wrecked on*
*The Beasts of Holm, Stornoway Harbour,*
*1st Jan. 1919: 205 lives lost*

'The tide now, rising or falling?'
'I think she's rising.'
'Aye, well, that's it then.'

Conglomerate backs of rock
awash then exposed
with the pulse of each
individual surf.
The nigh
to go round you.'
'Aye it goes right through you.'
Sure as shrapnel.

The grounded decking
also shedding
sailors like waters:
numbered reservists,
Hands and ABs;
a Petty Officer;
Cooper 2nd Class;
Signalman; Gunner.
Slipping or jumping.

Sometimes engaging
hard shoals
studded with
untidy scales.
Sometimes sliding
a choking gap
of troubled mudflats.

All assistance from
the wreck's own confines.
Lit by weak rockets.
Boots over first and
John Finlay towing
light stuff on a bowline.
Knocked-back under
the pretty counter.
He'd have to recognise
the top of a big one.

Achieving a shoreline.
The gasping few
mastering a belay:
*all who tried did not manage
to hold on*[1]
The sodden hemp hawser
out from broached steel
in grinding compression.
Bitter hands fast to
these three strands.

Late carts tilting
useless apparatus
over stoney fields

Three shapes hanging
on stretching tendons
to an arrow-shaft from
a broken-backed eagle.
Two slipped to blood
One held through dark
swept by spray and
the timed light
of irrelevant Amish.

All the dials
on a total island
seized at sunrise.
And soon the lot was offered for sale.
Pukka Burma teak.
Admiralty brass.
Unrecovered sons.

John Finlay resumed
his laying of keels.
Larch was clamped
tight as speech
to amount to
remembered shapes.
Fins and bellies
contributing to
seakeeping qualities[2].


1. *from the testimony of Robert Mackinnon,*
   *one of 79 survivors*
2. *John Finlay Macleod, boatbuilder, was*
   *honoured by The Royal Humane Society*

Kenneth C. Steven

## ARGYLL

All down the coast
The air was full of fish and sunset.

By nine the lemon-coloured cottages
Were warm windows glowing over the bays.

Far west the light a rim of blue and white,
Jura and Mull and Scarba all carved from shining.

On the way home we stopped to listen to the dark,
To the sea coming huge over a hundred beaches.

In among the trees, in windless stillness,
The bats were flitting, weaving patterns with the air.

That night I did not want the stars to rise at all,
I wanted it to be like this and nothing more

Looking west into the sunset
To the very end of the world.

## LOGIE

When I was a boy I went every Saturday
To the north end of the island,
To her farmhouse for eggs.

I walked against the wind
That was full of snowflakes
The salt knife of the sea.

When I got to her doorway
The collies flowed out at me
Black and white bounces barking.

She brought me into her home
Gave me six eggs in a box
To take back for the coming week.

Last night her son was drowned
Returning in a boat at midnight
He was lost and will not come home.

I am older and have been far away
In different corners of the world –
I have seen all that I expected.

But now I am returning to the island
I am going to the north end
To the woman who once gave me eggs.

And when I get there and the collies come round me
And I stand in the kitchen and see her
A whole ocean will drown me.

Ruaraidh MacThòmais

## LUCHD POILITICS

Luchd poilitics air an TV,
luchd poilitics air an spiorad:
tha e nas fhasa a bhith beò le na daoine sin
ann an leabhraichean eachdraidh
far an tèid do bhreith air a' mheidh,
socraichte le gliocas tìm,
ás aonais fèin-spèis
is faiteachan faoin
is mire ri camera.
Tha e cho math
nach eil Pitt is Gladstone,
gun luaidh air Caesar
no Jefferson
againn air video,
is cothrom againn
ar breith a thoirt gu ìre
fo chiùineas fad-seallaidh.

Derick Thomson

## POLITICIANS/WEIGHT OF POLITICS

Politicians on TV,
the weight of politics on the spirit:
it is easier to live with these people
in history books
where one can weigh the judgement,
settled by time's wisdom,
without self-regard
and silly smiles
and playing to the camera.
It's just as well
we don't have Pitt and Gladstone,
not to mention Caesar
or Jefferson
on video,
and that we can
come to a mature judgement
in the calm of the long view.

## MEURAN-NA-MNATHA-SIDHE

Seilleanan trang a' siubhal
meuranan na mnatha-sìdhe:
is cinnteach nach eil na tha sin
de mheuran oirre, is meuran air gach aon,
no a bheil an leas làn de mhnathan-sìdhe?
Dh'fheumadh tu coimpiutair fìor làidir
gu cùnntadh na tha sin de mhnathan-sìdhe
air feadh na dùthcha,
's gach tè trang le snàthad is snàithlean
a' cumail an t-saoghail an òrdugh,
ach dhan t-seillean
chan eil an sin ach faoineas,
tha a choimpiutair fhèin aig'
's a shaoghal air a riaghladh
eadar sgeap is meuran
gus an tuit iad uile gu talamh.

## FOXGLOVE

Busy bees exploring
the foxgloves/the fairy's thimbles:
surely she doesn't have as many fingers as that,
with a thimble on each one,
or is the garden full of fairies?
You would need a really powerful computer
to count all the fairies
in the country,
each one of them busy with needle and thread
keeping the world in order,
but for the bee
that's a lot of nonsense,
it has its own computer
and its world is controlled
between hive and thimble
until they all drop to the ground.

Valerie Thornton

## DISTANCE

You are as lost to me
as you were dead.

By mistake
in my heart-pocket
I bring your image
smiling love at me
from that ruined chapel
on Bute, to here,
within this hollow cairn
on Knockside Hill
from where I see
framed in space
between stones, Bute,
the south end
with the ruined chapel
where you smile at me

until a sniping wind blinds
and chills me to the heart.

**Gael Turnbull**

## DON'T TELL ME

Don't tell me it's to be expected,
    is only natural, as ongoing
as the succession of the seasons,
    as the rotation of the galaxies
or that this blur
    is an effect of refraction,
of excessive fluid on the cornea,
    or this darkness a shift of isobars,
convection currents, humidity,
    a weather front obscuring the sun
when all the words mean nothing
    and there's only
this absence where you were,
    this weight of silence
as after thunder, these roots
    torn from the earth.

**Billy Watt**

## WATCHING THE WORLD CUP FINAL IN FLORIDA

Ronaldo's story runs on ABC
between the ads for cars and credit cards
while, overhead, green clouds flick lizard tongues
and thunder hammers faster than your pulse.

As Pele smiles from the commentary box
we garage the car, strap down the plastic benches;
crickets cling to the net around our pool
and palms begin to shake like shamen's wands.

In fire-engine red at the foot of the screen
we learn that Tampa Bay is hit by storm.
Pele fidgets, a restless Buddha now,
as Zinedine Zidane pulls strings midfield:

Brazilian shirts are yellow petals
scattered in blue hail. A voice cuts in to say
which multinational has brought us all
this segment of the game commercial-free.

At last Brazil begin to mesmerise:
Roberto Carlos strikes a looping shot –
but then Zidane has arrowed in for France.
Ronaldo limps back upfield, breathing fast.

Our air-vents leak the smell of something burning
as Zagallo, the little ant, entreats
his team – but again Zidane's in space. Two-nil.
The commentator's incoherent now.

The half-time news from Channel Nine. A Sheriff's
car reads Referee. Two boys climb in.
A girl has killed her mother. Sharks provide
a cure for cancer. Next the Golf World Cup.

France have dazzled. Brazil are frazzled.
We watch on, hoping that the power will last,
as the onscreen map blips forward, Hillsborough
from Polk. The sky is curdled charcoal.

'Can this really be happening?' we hear.
'The World Cup Final and Brazil shut out?'
Dugarry passes from defence. Petit.
Three-nil. 'It's in the freezer. France are rocking!'

Didier Deschamps, the water-carrier,
that red band on his chest an Indian brave's,
lifts up the trophy. Team-mates kiss, raise fists –
then Pele punches air for Mastercard

and, unpredictably, the storm dips south
of us. We hear the pent-up breath released
of cars on the interstate. Damp heat clamps down;
frogs start to croak; ants scurry by the poolside.

Inside, we watch the litter of clouds blow past,
though another front waits down by Mexico.
Then portents: two tall, graceful waterbirds
strut on tip-toe along the empty street.

Tread softly, you birds: for you tread on our screens.

Christopher Whyte

## FAD' AN DÈIDH DHUINN CAOCHLADH ...

Fad' an dèidh dhuinn caochladh, bithidh sinn
a' nochdadh ann an aislingean ar càirdean

an aodach nach robh againn riamh, 's ag ràdh
bhriathran nach aithnich sinn, a' dèiligeadh

ri pearsachan nach robh sinn eòlach orra,
sùgradh 's a' gràdhachadh le feòil nach maireann

mar gum b' e actairean a bh' annainn, ann
am film a sgrìobh neach eile, is ar pàirt

cho neònach is gum feòraich sinn an e
ar co-shamhladh a th' ann. Ach tha a' chùis

mòran nas sìmplidhe. Is e gum bi
sinn marbh, agus na bruadaraichean beò.

**Translation: Meg Bateman**

## LONG AFTER WE ARE GONE ...

Long after we are gone,
we'll appear in the dreams of our friends,

dressed in clothes we never wore,
speaking words we never spoke,

held by people we never saw –
flesh caressed that is no more,

like actors in a film, our parts so strange
we'll hardly know ourselves ...

yet not so strange, for we'll be dead
and our dreamers alive.

## B' E SIN SAMHRADH NAN IOMADH BÀS

B' e sin samhradh nan iomadh bàs. An toiseach,
bàs na bana-charaid anns an Spàinn,
ag abachadh mar bhraon de dh'uisge anns
an adhar chlaoidhteach, bhruthainneach, a' gabhail
tiughaid agus truime gus an robh i
deiseil airson sileadh, gun aon fhuaim.
Shiubhail i gu sìothchainteach, gun dùsgadh,
dìreach mar gum b' e roimh-bhlas den bhàs
a bh' anns a' chungaidh-leigheis chaidh a stealladh
a-steach dha cuislean, gus a fulangas
a lùghdachadh, 's a dh'fhàg na cadal i.
Cha do chaochail mo mhàthair, ach bha 'm bàs
trang a' toirt dhuinn shanasan air fhaisge,
chan ann a-mhàin a' milleadh dath a' chraicinn
air cùl nan làmh a bha cho dìcheallach,
air neo nach biodh i siubhal ach le bata
air neo a buidhre, 's gun do dhiùlt i fhathast
inneal sam bith a chur na cluais, air neo
an sealladh iongantach a nochdadh air
a gnùis nuair a bhiodh i a' sireadh facail
nach fhoillsichte dhi, mar gun robh i dùsgadh,
is i 'na leanabh uair eil', ann an dùthaich
nach fhac i gus an t-àm. Ach b' e an sanas
a bu chudthromaiche air dlùthachadh
a bàis caomhalachd ùr nach b' urrainn dhi
a tùs no bun a shoilleireachadh dhuinn,
's a bha cho nàdarra dhi 'n uair sin, 's dòcha
mar a bha i gun eisimpleir nar sùilean.
Bha rudan do-sheallta a' bàsachadh
aig an aon àm, ceangal nam measg, is breug
fhalaichte ga chaitheamh beag is beag,
ròpa m' earbsa a' cnàmhadh gus na chaill
mi m' acarsaid is nach robh agam ach
an doimhne mhòr, is bhris am bàs a-steach
dom bhruadaran. Bha mi an caisteal àrd,
sa Ghearmailt, 's dòcha, beanntan timcheall air,
a rinneadh anns an linn seo chaidh, 's e làn
de dh' obair shnaidht' air dòigh na Meadhan Aois'.
Bha sinn air leth na h-oidhche a chur seachad
le fleadhachas is dannsa, 's chaidh mi chadal
ann an seòmar air an làr a b' àirde,
dìreach fo mhullach daingeann, trom a' chaisteil.

Dhùisg mi anns a' chamhanaich, is mhothaich
mi air ball do sgòthannan nan speur,
a chunnaic mi tro shailthean brist' a' mhullaich.
Cha robh an caisteal ach 'na làrach, luibhean
a' fàs mun cuairt orm, feannagan ri gràgail.
Thuig mi gun robh iad uile marbh, na daoin'
a chuir mi 'n oidhche seachad ann am measg.
Thòisich mi 'g èigheachd, oir bha eagal orm,
an dèidh dhomh dùsgadh anns an fhìrinneachd,
gun siùbhlainn am measg daoine marbh, gun fhios.

## Translation

# THAT WAS THE SUMMER OF MANY DEATHS

That was the summer of many deaths:
first, the death of a friend in Spain,
swelling like a water-drop in a thunderous sky,
until silently ready to drop.
She died peacefully, without waking,
as if that injection to lessen her pain and let her sleep
had been a foretaste of death.

My mother didn't die, but death was busy
giving warnings of its presence:
brown blotches on the backs
of her ever-active hands,
her need for a stick,
her deafness (and resistance to a hearing-aid),
the look of surprise in her face
like a child walking in a strange land
when a word eluded her,
and, most noticeable, a new gentleness,
which seemed completely natural to her
though she could not explain its origins
and it had never been a part of her before.

Invisible things were dying at the same time,
a hidden lie worn down, bit by bit,
my rope of trust worn away till I slipped my moorings
with now only the open sea before me,
and death broke into my dreams.

I was in a high castle, maybe in Germany,
with medieval stonework and mountains all round,
and after a night of dancing and feasting,
I went to sleep in the topmost room,
below its heavy battlements.
At dawn I woke to see clouds through broken rafters,
the castle a ruin, weeds growing round me, crows croaking,
and those people with whom I had feasted and danced
all dead ...
I started screaming having woken to the terror,
that I might move unknowingly through the dead.

Rachel Yule

## CAVE CANEM

(passages in italics should be read in pedantic Edinburgh Scenglish)

As you can aw see –
If you're no blin –
A'm a dug:
A big, black, barkin dug,
A slinkin, snappin, snarlin dug;
An this is ma patch.
An that reid-roostit Ford pickup
Wi nae back wheels
An the door hingin aff the hinges
Is ma den.

*I've seen better times.*
*In my – em-m – salad days*
*I was companion to a professor emeritus,*
*A scholar and a gentleman,*
*An Egyptologist.*
*When introducing me to former colleagues,*
*He used to say,*
*'I've named him Anubis. Come closer*
*And observe the set and shape of his ears.'*
That was the sign for me tae gurr
Deep doon in ma thrapple;
Ma birse rose an ma fangs flashed.
They louped back, teeth chatterin.
*'He's a one man dog,' my old boy smirked.*

Oh, it was barrie – a dug's life:
Wee private jokes an every creature comfort;
Till yae day, efter a brisk constitutional
In the Queen's Park,
When he was pourin the pre-prandial sherry
He drappit doon, deid.
A was oot o ma skull, barkin mad:
A lickit his face an yowled in his lug;
But he was ayont the aid o man or beast.
So A lappit up the Tio Pepe.

*I'm not proud of what happened next:*
*Perhaps it was the drink;*
*And the walk had given me an appetite;*
*And pangs of hunger dull the finer sensibilities;*
*And the name Anubis has connotations.*
Onywey, efter A had reenged roon
The hale hoose an fund naethin tae eat
But a half packet o broken shortbreid,
A broke the last taboo.

A was that schizoid
A squeezed through the dug-flap
*(The egress he constructed with his own hands*
*For my convenience when I was a little puppy,*
*Not quite house-trained).*

Then A louped the back dyke,
An hid ma shame in Bawsinch
Amang the wee trees
In the Native Species Nursery.
*I really should have had counselling.*

*There were beast sightings*
*Behind the Sheep's Heid Inn;*
*A Guided Walk of very mature students*
*Broke into a canter*
*Along the Innocent Railway.*
*Park Rangers, safe in their vans,*
*Screamed into their mobile phones,*
*'SOS! Emergency! SOS!*
*Send in the men from the Zoo!'*

Land Rovers screamed roond the Windy Gowl;
A scarpered, an had juist about reached
The sanctuary o the Foxes' Holes
When there was a sting in ma arse –
A mere flea-bite;
Ma brain birled;
Ma legs buckled;
Samson's Ribs crumbled;
The sky blackened.

A cam roond in Seafield, c/o SSPCA.
'A'll hae that bugger,' the wee man swore.
'You quite sure? He's a killer.'
'Juist whit A'm needin.
When A got hame last nicht
Ma yaird wis hoachin wi Polis
Vandalisin upholstery, slashin tyres.'
He chucked me a bluidy great steak,
Then put the boot in ma ribs.
'He'll no bite the haun that feeds him,'
The wee nyaff gittered.
'Whit dae they cry him?'
'Anubis.' 'Whit a name for a dug!'
He luftit a bucket o cauld, dirty water.
'A hereby re-christen him, Saddam.'
Ma e'en nipped. A stank o cats.

A keep ma heid doon:
A'm a pack animal
An he's the leader o the pack – *pro tem*
*(As my old mentor was wont to say).*
A'm bidin ma time.
When ma day comes
A'll no bite the haun that feeds me;
A'll go for the jugular.

# BIOGRAPHIES

Leila Aboulela grew up in Khartoum and since 1990 has been living in Aberdeen. Her stories have been broadcast on BBC Radio and published in *New Scottish Writing 1997* (HarperCollins) and *Ahead Of Its Time* (Cape). Her first novel, *The Translator*, is published by Polygon.

Meg Bateman, born Edinburgh 1959. Learnt Gaelic at university and South Uist. Taught at Aberdeen University for seven years, then Sabhal Mòr Ostaig in Skye where she lives with her son. Her collection, *Aotromachd / Lightness 1997*, won an SAC Book Award and was also short-listed for the Stakis Prize.

Gavin Bowd's first full-length collection of poems, *Technique*, was published in 1999 by Dionysia Press. His poetry, fiction, translations and essays have appeared in numerous places, including *Edinburgh Review*, *Shorts*, *The Eildon Tree*, *Europe* and *Digraphe*.

Tom Bryan was born Canada, 1950. Long-resident in Scotland (Wester Ross). Widely published, anthologised, broadcast poet and short story writer. Editor (*Northwords*, *Broken Fiddle*, anthologies). Current writer-in-residence for Scottish Borders. Founded, edits *The Eildon Tree* in Selkirk. Previous *New Writing Scotland 12, 16*. Two poetry collections, *Wolfwind* (Chapman, 1996), *North East Passage* (SCP, 1996).

Ron Butlin has published five books of poetry, a collection of short stories, *The Tilting Room* and two novels, *The Sound of my Voice* and *Night Visits*. His work has been translated into over ten languages. He lives in Edinburgh with his wife and their dog.

Angus Calder's book of poems is *Waking in Waikato* (Diehard). Otherwise, polemical journalist, critic and historian: his latest publication is an anthology, *Wars*, for Penguin, of prose and verse about war in twentieth-century Europe. He lives in Edinburgh.

Maoilios M. Caimbeul (Myles Campbell) was born March 23, 1944 in Skye. Collections of verse include *Bailtean* 1987 (bilingual) and *A' Gabhail Ris* 1994 (Gaelic only). His poetry has won several awards, including first for *Thar na Starsnaich* in the 1998 Gaelic section of the Laoghaire-Rathdown international poetry competition. He also writes children's fiction.

Stuart B. Campbell originates from Lanarkshire, but now lives in Portsoy, Aberdeenshire. His poetry has been published in a wide variety of literary journals and anthologies. A first collection, *Robie Gow's Prison* was published in 1996. He edited *Things Not Seen – an anthology of Scottish Mountain Poetry*, published in June 1999.

Stewart Conn lives in Edinburgh. He has had work in several issues of *New Writing Scotland*. In May he took part in the Festival Franco-anglaise de Poésie, in Paris. His selected poems *Stolen Light* (Bloodaxe Books, Newcastle) were launched during this year's Edinburgh Book Festival.

Anna Crowe lives in St Andrews, working as a translator and creative-writing teacher. Her first collection of poems, *Skating out of the House*, was published by Peterloo in 1997. She won the Peterloo Open Poetry Competition in 1993 and 1997. Her work has been translated into Catalan.

David Cunningham was born in Ayrshire in December 1970. He was educated at Marr College and at Glasgow University, from which he has an MA (Hons) in English Language and Literature and a PhD in Scottish Literature. His stories have appeared in the *London Magazine*, *Northwords* and on BBC Radio 4.

Jenni Daiches was born in Chicago, and has lived in Scotland since 1971. Published poetry includes *Mediterranean* (Scottish Cultural press, 1995) and contributions to mainly Scottish magazines and collections. As Jenni Calder, writes on literary and historical subjects. Lives in South Queensferry and works at the National Museums of Scotland.

Robert Davidson was born in Glasgow but is long-time resident in Ross-shire. He has published two collections of poetry, *The Bird and The Monkey* and *Total Immersion*, and edited a third, *After the Watergaw*. He is Secretary of the Neil Gunn Memorial Trust and Reviews Editor of *Northwords* magazine.

Martin Donnelly was born in Glasgow in 1977. He is presently working on a novel, *White Collar Blues*, about all the offices and people he has passed through since 1995.

Anne Donovan lives and teaches in Glasgow. Short stories published in *New Writing Scotland*, *A Braw Brew*, *Chapman* and the *Flamingo Book of New Scottish Writing*. Winner of the 1997 *Macallan / Scotland on Sunday* short story competition.

John Duffy is a Glaswegian living in Huddersfield; one of the Albert Poets, who perform, run workshops, and organise readings in and beyond West Yorkshire. He has two collections, *Troika 1* and *Perpetual Light*.

Rhoda Dunbar belongs to Inverness-shire and now lives there again after several years working in Edinburgh and Aberdeen. Native language: Standard English. Has had poems and stories in northern publications.

R.J. Ford grew up in Scotland and now lives in the London area.

Moira Forsyth lives in Dingwall. She writes poetry and fiction. Her first collection of poetry *What the Negative Reveals* was published by ArtTm this year, and her first novel, *Waiting for Lindsay*, by Hodder in July 1999.

Paul Foy is a native Glaswegian who now lives and teaches in Aberdeen. He has had work published in *Full Strength Angels: New Writing Scotland 14* and *MICA*, and accepted by *Chapman* for imminent publication.

Anne C. Frater was born in the Isle of Lewis in 1967. Completed a PhD on early Scottish Gaelic women's poetry in 1995. Poetry published in several anthologies, including *An aghaidh na siorraidheachd* and *Dreamstate*. Collection of poems, *Fo'n t-Slige* (Gairm) published in 1995. Also contributed a chapter to *A History of Scottish Women's Writing*. Currently based in Glasgow.

Raymond Friel lives in Somerset with his wife and three sons. He is Head of English in a secondary school in Trowbridge. *Renfrewshire in Old Photographs*, a co-written pamphlet of poems, is forthcoming from Mariscat Press. He is an editor of the cultural review *Southfields*.

Robin Fulton's poems have in recent years been appearing in Swedish, German, Spanish and Hebrew versions. His own latest translations are *Tomas Tranströmer's New Collected Poems* (Bloodaxe) and *Five Swedish Poets* (Norvik), both 1997.

Valerie Gillies, Poet. Publications include *Tweed Journey*, *The Chanter's Tune* (both Canongate), and *The Ringing Rock* (Scottish Cultural Press). Her new collection, *Lightning Prints*, will be published in 2000. Currently working on *Men and Beasts*, an exhibition with the photographer Rebecca Marr, for which they have received an SAC Cross-Media award.

Jules Horne was born in 1963 in Hawick. She studied German and French at Oxford. Currently working as a broadcast journalist for Swiss Radio International in Bern.

John Hudson's second collection of poems, *Canny Tongues*, is due later this year. He edits *Markings* magazine and publications, and edited *The Collected Poems of William Nicholson*, published by GC Books earlier this year. He also teaches, writes criticism, screenplays, works as a freelance copywriter, installation artist and events organiser.

Jim Hughes was born in Ayrshire in 1930. Having spent most of his working life in industry and education, he is now a Visiting Professor at Strathclyde University. He has come recently to writing prose and poetry. *Comma*, from a growing collection, is his first published poem.

Robert Hume was born and brought up in Glasgow. After getting his English degree from Glasgow University, he taught English briefly in Hawick, then moved school to teach in Biggar. He still teaches there but now lives in Carluke, and writes both prose and poetry, in Scots and English.

George Inglis was born in 1958 and lives in Bridge of Weir. After being medically discharged from the Fire Service, he studied Scottish Literature at the university of Glasgow. He now works as an administrator. Although he has had a few articles published, *Jean and Mary on a Tree* is his first published short story.

Helen Lamb – poet and short story writer. Poetry collection *Strange Fish* published by Duende, 1997. Work has also been widely published in anthologies and magazines, and broadcast on BBC Radio 4, Radio Scotland and RTE.

Maurice Lindsay was born in Glasgow in 1918. Educated Glasgow Academy, Scottish National Academy of Music; Junior Staff College, army, 9th Cameronians then War Office. Director, Scottish Civic Trust 1967–83; Hon. Secretary-General, Europe Nostrum, 1983–90. Books include *Collected Poems 1940–90*, *News of the World*, *Speaking Likenesses* and *The Burns Encyclopaedia*. Forthcoming – *Worlds Apart* and *Fabric of a City: Glasgow*.

Peter McCarey works in Geneva. *Sapristi!* is from *Fear of Chaos*, which is looking for a publisher. His poetry includes *In the Metaforest* (1999) and *The Devil in the Driving Mirror* (1995) – both Vennel Press – and *Town Shanties* (1990). *Prerr Wheel* (version one) is ready to roll on the web.

J Derrick McClure, Senior Lecturer, Department of English, University of Aberdeen. Author of *Why Scots Matters, Scots and its Literature, Scotland o Gael an Lawlander* (a volume of Scots translations from contemporary Gaelic poetry), *Language, Poetry and Nationhood* and numerous articles and papers. Chairman of the Forum for Research in the Languages of Scotland and Ulster, and editor of *Scottish Language*.

Euan McCulloch was born in 1970 and grew up in the Glasgow area. His first collection *This Time of Day* was published in 1996 by Akros and reprinted in 1998. He is currently preparing his second collection.

Janina MacDonald was born in St Abbs, Berwickshire. Educated at Eyemouth and the Berwickshire High Schools and thereafter at the Royal Scottish Academy of Music and Drama, Glasgow. Musician, mother, housewife and at present a student of Creative Writing at Edinburgh University's Centre of Continuing Education. She lives in South Queensferry.

Murdo Stal MacDonald has recently returned to his native Isle of Lewis where he now lives and works. He and his wife Cath have two children, Daisy and Samuel.

James McGonigal was born in 1947 in Dumfries. He taught English in secondary schools and then in teacher education, currently in the University of Glasgow. A previous editor of *New Writing Scotland*, he has published literary and educational essays, as well as short stories and two collections of poetry: *Unidentified Flying Poems* (1981) and *Driven Home*.

Hamish Whyte was born in 1947 in Giffnock and lives in Glasgow. He has edited several anthologies including *Mungo's Tongues: Glasgow Poems 1630–1990* (1993) and *An Arran Anthology* (1997). He runs the Mariscat Press and is currently translating Martial, Books XIII and XIV.

Rob Mackenzie was born in Glasgow in 1964. He has also lived in Aberdeen, Edinburgh and Seoul. He plays with Glasgow avant rock band *Plastic Chicken* and forms part of Media and Mood Music collective, *McCafferty, Mackenzie, Smith and Moller*. Currently, he is writing a novel and more poems.

Donal McLaughlin was born in Northern Ireland. He moved to Scotland as a child. *Surviving Uncertain Fates* – his third appearance in *New Writing Scotland* – is the seventh story to be published from a collection nearing completion. Donal also translates from German.

Anne Macleod has four children, lives on the Black Isle and works as a dermatologist, travelling through the Highlands. Her first poetry collection *Standing by Thistles* (Scottish Cultural Press) was shortlisted for the 1997 Saltire First Book of the Year Award. *Just the Caravaggio* (Poetry Salzburg) appeared in 1999.

Aonghas MacNeacail is a poet, scriptwriter, journalist and playwright who was born on the Isle of Skye in 1942.

Kevin MacNeil is a widely published writer of poetry and prose. First recipient of the Iain Crichton Smith Writing Fellowship. Currently living in Skye writing a novel, etc. *Love and Zen in the Outer Hebrides* is available from Canongate Books.

John S. MacPherson was born on the Canadian prairie to a family of Islay and Skye descent. Youth spent among old Canadian Gaels in Alberta and PEI and French literature snobs at university. Taught French immersion and is now a lecturer at Sabhal Mòr Ostaig in Skye.

John Maley was born in Glasgow in 1962. He has published poetry and fiction in previous editions of *New Writing Scotland*. *Papa and Mama* forms part of a short story collections centred around a Glasgow gay bar. He has just completed his first novel, *Stein and the Siren*.

Andy Manders is from Perthshire. A graduate of the creative writing programme at Glasgow University, his work appears in a variety of magazines and journals. He is currently not writing a novel.

Joseph Mills has had stories published in various anthologies, including Serpent's Tail's *The Ten Commandments* and *The Picador Book of Contemporary Scottish Fiction*. His first novel, *Towards the End*, was published by Polygon. A novella and collection of short stories *Obsessions* was published by Millivres in 1998.

Donald S. Murray is from Ness, Isle of Lewis, and is Principal Teacher of English at Sgoil Lionacleit, Benbecula. His short-story collection, *Special Deliverance* (Scottish Cultural Press), was shortlisted for the Saltire Society First Book Award in 1998 and his poetry has appeared in various publications.

Jan Natanson was educated at St Andrews. Lives in Kirriemuir. Short stories and poetry in Scots and English published in various magazines and anthologies. Also writes non-fiction, and for film and television. Edits *Lallans* magazine. Mostly writes for theatre, however. Currently under commission to Byre Theatre, St Andrews.

William Neill (b. 1922, Ayrshire), writer in Gaelic, Scots and English. Frequent publication in most Scots literary magazines and some in England, Ireland, Wales and the Continent. Ten verse collections in Scotland, one in Ireland, one in Denmark, one in Italy. Has had grants for literary work and translation from the Scottish Arts Council.

Stuart A. Paterson was born 1966 Cornwall, raised in Ayrshire. Lives in Lancashire with his partner Eejay; employed as a resident social worker. *Saving Graces* published, 1997, by Diehard. Former Gregory Award winner, SAC Writing Fellow for Dumfries and Galloway. Fan of Kilmarnock FC, Cumnock Juniors but _never_ Auchinleck Talbot.

Tom Pow is the author of three books of poems: *Rough Seas*, *The Moth Trap* (Canongate) and *Red Letter Day* (Bloodaxe). With the artist Hugh Bryden he runs Cacafuego Press. Their first publication, *Landscapes*, was both launched and exhibited at last summer's Edinburgh Book Festival. He teaches part-time.

Christopher John Roberts was born in Greenock in 1961 and now lives in Angus with his wife and three children. He has been published in *New Scottish Writing 1997* (HarperCollins/SAC) and is currently working on a novel for children and a sequence of inter-related stories set in contemporary Scotland.

James Robertson is the author of two books of short stories, *Close* (1991) and *The Ragged Man's Complaint* (1993), and two collections of poetry, *Sound-Shadow* (1995) and *I Dream of Alfred Hitchcock* (1999). His first novel, *The Fanatic*, will be published in 2000 by Fourth Estate.

Dilys Rose was born and brought up in Glasgow and now lives in Edinburgh. She has published two books of poetry, three of short stories and, most recently, a novel, *Pest Maiden*.

Suhayl Saadi is a Glasgow-based novelist and short story writer. In 1997, first published under a pseudonym and he won a major prize in the Bridport Short Story Competition. Short prose has been widely published. Was one of the judges of the Calendar Poetry Competition 1999. Between live readings and radio appearances, he is working on another novel.

Ian Stephen is a former Coastguard officer, now artist. His work is realised in several mediums, usually involving language and always assuming the triumph of the vernacular.

Kenneth C. Steven was born in Glasgow in 1968 but has spent most of his life thus far in Highland Perthshire. It is the people and landscape of the north that have inspired the bulk of his fiction and poetry to date. He is currently reader-in-residence for Aberdeen City Council.

Derick Thomson (in Gaelic Ruaraidh MacThòmais), born Isle of Lewis 1921. Taught at Edinburgh, Aberdeen and Glasgow Universities. Published widely, in Gaelic and English. Editor of *Gairm* 1952–. Collected poems *Creachadh na Clàrsaich / Plundering the Harp* and the latest collection *Meall Garbh / The Rugged Mountain* available from Gairm Publications, Glasgow.

Valerie Thornton writes poems and short stories. She works as a creative writing tutor. In 1989 she received and SAC Writer's Bursary, and in 1992 was shortlisted for the SoS / Macallan Short Story Prize. her creative writing textbook, *Working Words*, won joint first prize as TESS / Saltire Society Scottish Educational Book of the Year 1996.

Gael Turnbull's most recent publications include *A Rattle of Scree* (Akros), *Transmutations* (Shoestring) and *Amorous Greetings* (Vennel).

Billy Watt was born in Greenock and now lives in West Lothian, where he works at Broxburn Academy. He divides his writing time fairly evenly between poetry and fiction.

Christopher Whyte shared a Saltire Award for his first collection of Gaelic poems in 1992. His poems and translations have been widely published. He edited *An Aghaidh na Sìorraidheachd: Ochdnar Bhàrd Ghàidhlig / In the Face of Eternity: Eight Gaelic Poets* and is the author of three novels in English. The second, *The Warlock of Strathearn*, won an SAC prize in 1998. He lives in Edinburgh and teaches in Glasgow University.

Rachel Yule is a native of Carnwath. She taught English in schools in Lanark, London, Glasgow and Edinburgh, then switched to Further Education. Now retired, she is enjoying the activities of Edinburgh Writer's Club and Broadside (Women Playwrights in Scotland).